QUASARS, REDSHIFTS AND CONTROVERSIES

QUASARS, REDSHIFTS, AND CONTROVERSIES

Halton Arp

Interstellar Media
2153 Russell Street
Berkeley, CA 94705

Interstellar Media

2153 Russell Street
Berkeley, CA 94705

Library of Congress Catalog Card Number 87-080290

ISBN 0-941325-00-8
Printed in the United States of America

9 8 7 6 5 4 3 2

TABLE OF CONTENTS

PREFACE

The purpose of this book is to present important information about the nature of the universe in which we live. Knowledge of the laws of nature offers humankind the only chance of survival in a changing environment. It endows us with the power to achieve whatever we consider our most desirable evolutionary goals. Perhaps most of all, the search for knowledge gives expression to a basic curiosity which appears to be the salient defining characteristic of human beings.

The information about the physical universe that this book tries to convey is highly controversial. Since I believe that the facts are true and important, and since I have first-hand knowledge of the observations, I have undertaken to present the subject in the following book. Actually, this offers the only possibility of discussing this subject in a meaningful way at this time. The reasons for this are the following:

First, the antecedent observations have been published over a span of twenty years in various technical, astronomical journals. In order to construct a coherent picture, these reports need now to be drawn together and related to each other. In the past, it has always been possible to criticize or ignore individual discoveries and avoid the weight of accumulated evidence which a minority of astronomers have felt requires a drastic change in current assumptions about the universe. This book presents an integrated picture of this evidence which it is hoped will be compelling enough to establish the necessity for a new and large step forward in astronomical concepts.

Secondly, there have recently been attempts by a few people in the field to suppress new results that disagree with their particular viewpoint. Telescope time needed to follow up discoveries in these directions has been denied. Research reports to journals have been rejected or modified by referees committed to the status quo. It is clear that when scientific results are prevented from appearing or being discussed in standard journals, the only alternative is to publish a book. Then no one who is interested is denied the opportunity of reading the evidence. Since many generalist readers are also interested in this subject, I have tried to write in a way that is comprehensible to nontechnical readers. Then no one, specialist or generalist, will be denied access to this new information if they wish to make use of it.

I believe in order to gain the most fundamental knowledge of which we are capable it is necessary to continually and sincerely question our assumptions and test our theories. In a sense, the way we do science is more important than the exact results at any given moment. I have stated the results as correctly as I can in this book but one must always face the possibility that one's current understanding is more or less completely wrong. So, even if my thesis were mistaken—which I consider unlikely in view of the evidence—it may still have been valuable to have discussed how the process of astronomical discovery is actually conducted. The most important thing for us to recall may be, that the crucial quality of science is to encourage, not discourage, the testing of assumptions. That is the only ethic that will eventually start us on our way to a new and much deeper level of understanding.

INTRODUCTION

Redshifts and
the Hubble Law

In 1924, Edwin Hubble demonstrated that the small, hazy patches of light we see in the sky on a dark night—the galaxies—are really enormous islands of billions of stars, like our own Milky Way galaxy seen at a great distance. Study with large telescopes revealed that the fainter and smaller a galaxy appeared, the higher, in general, was its redshift. Redshift describes the fact that the characteristic lines in its spectrum due to hydrogen, calcium, and other elements appear at longer (redder) wavelengths than in a terrestrial laboratory. This effect was most simply attributed to a recession velocity of the emitting source—like the falling pitch of a receding train whistle. It was therefore concluded that the fainter and smaller the galaxy, the more distant it was, and the faster it was flying away from us. This is the velocity interpretation of the redshift-apparent brightness relation, the standard interpretation of the so-called Hubble law.

About this time, Einstein was writing equations that attempted to describe the behavior of the entire universe, the totality of what exists. His equations pointed to its probable instability. Gravitation was either strong enough to be in the process of contracting the universe or too weak to prevent its expansion. In view of the extant conclusions about galaxy recession velocities, it was natural to interpret them as due to expansion of the universe. Extrapolating these velocities back to an origin in time gave rise to the concept of the universe being born in a primeval explosion, the so-called "big bang" cosmology.

If this simple theory could explain all the observations, as it appeared to do for many years, then it would be what people strive for—an elegant solution. But it is my thesis in this book that from 1966 onward, observations began to accumulate that could not be explained by this conventional picture. Some extragalactic objects had to have redshifts which were not caused by velocity of recession.

At the very least, it seemed that some modification had to be made to the current theory. The reaction against these discordant observations among some influential specialists was very strong: It was said that they "violated the known laws of physics" and therefore must be incorrect. Alas, it seems that in the intervening years the useful hypothesis had become enshrined dogma.

Translated plainly, this dogma simply states: "At this golden moment in human history, we know all the important aspects of nature that we will ever know. In spite of a long record of fundamental revolutions in human thought, there are now no surprises, there is now an end to this history." This seems patently absurd. In fact, like most people, I would instinctively have a kind of temporal Copernican view that no arbitrary epoch is special. I believe that startling forward leaps in knowledge will continue to take place if the human race survives long enough. Nevertheless, I do not believe we can use extrapolation of past experience as a proof that this is taking place at any given moment. We must instead have concrete, specific evidence if a radical change is now needed. Therefore, my major goal in this book is to gather together all the proof existing at this moment, to show that there is massive, incontrovertible evidence for important phenomena and processes, perhaps even new forces or laws, which we cannot currently understand or explain.

In order to force a change in the current paradigm, this book presents observations in detail. Unlike the current belief in the field that observations can be accepted or discarded according to whether they fit a theory, I submit that the observations in fact *are* the known laws of physics. It only is required for us to connect them together in some satisfactory way. In this process, however, the one thing we must guard against is the misinterpretation of chance occurrences. (Throughout history this has been a popular activity called superstition.) Therefore, in each of the many examples I discuss, I first try to establish that if the observation is not a chance occurrence, then a fundamental "law" has been broken. For example, if a high-redshift object occurs close by in space to a low-redshift object, then the redshift-distance relation has been violated. This reduces the proof to a yes

or no decision. Either the closeness on the sky is an accidental projection of background and foreground objects, or there is a real physical proximity. We can then concentrate on determining how small the chance is that this observation is an accident. Even more important, we can determine whether there are other independent observations that support and confirm the reality of this result. Ultimately, each reader has to make his own decision whether the conventional law has been contradicted. But if we can gather enough different kinds of examples, as this book attempts to do, then perhaps we can achieve agreement that the phenomena are real. Then perhaps we can begin to discern repetitive patterns or similarities in the evidence that can be used to predict further examples and induce new hypotheses which could explain the phenomena. We will be underway into a new era.

The first shock to conventional theory came with the advent of radio astronomy and the discovery of quasars. Therefore, we should first define the terms relating to these subjects.

Radio Galaxies and Quasars

The story of this new branch of astronomy begins for me on a bluff overlooking the ocean on the east coast of Australia, near the end of the Second World War. The operator of a radar station noticed a source of radio noise in the sky that rose 3 minutes and 56 seconds earlier each day. An astronomer immediately recognizes that this is just the amount the stars gain on the sun each day (sidereal time runs "faster" than solar time). This motion marked the source of radio noise as belonging to the realm of the stars and galaxies. That original observer, John Bolton, went on to help found the science of radio astronomy and direct some of the early radio observatories. The original radio source was in the southern constellation of Centaurus and became known as Cen A. Eventually, thousands upon thousands of cosmic radio sources were discovered. Many of them were eventually identified with disturbed or active galaxies like the galaxy responsible for Cen A. The radio emission is caused by charged particles moving in a magnetic field. Both the charging of the particles (their ionization) and their motion is a result of high temperatures and energetic events.

These discoveries have required a fundamental change of concept about galaxies, a change that I believe has not yet been fully appreciated. It is no longer possible to view galaxies simply as relatively quiescent aggregates of stars, gas, and dust, all swirling in some majestic, ordered rotation about their center. Some are ripped asunder by huge explosions. Many have nuclei that vary strongly in brightness and intermittently eject quantities of matter outwards into space. In some ways, galaxies individually are reminiscent of the model of the universe as an exploding, or unfolding "cosmic egg." In my opinion, these new facts about the active nature of galaxies have not yet been integrated into a coherent picture of galaxy creation and evolution.

But among radio sources that were identified with visible objects, an even more mysterious class than radio galaxies was found. These were the quasars. Optically they looked like point sources of light—like stars—hence their name "quasi-stellar" radio source, a term soon shortened to quasar. The first of these objects was identified by Allan Sandage and Thomas Matthews in 1963 in a collaboration between an optical and a radio astronomer. Then Maarten Schmidt, an astronomer at Caltech, found the key to the spectrum by showing the initially puzzling lines were those of familiar elements but shifted very far to the red. This was the shock. Why, when the highest redshifted galaxies known had maximum redshifts of 20 to 40 percent the velocity of light, did these stellar-looking objects suddenly appear with redshifts of 80 or 90 per-

cent the velocity of light? It was briefly considered whether some other mechanism than velocity of recession could be responsible for quasar redshifts. For example, redshifting (which is equivalently a loss of energy of a photon) might by caused by a very strong gravitational field. Such explanations were quickly discarded, however, and it was decided that quasars were the most luminous objects in the universe, seen at such great distances that the expansion of the universe was giving them the largest possible recession velocities.

Difficulties were encountered almost immediately. In the first place, how could an object be so luminous? There was a problem of creating so much energy from known kinds of galaxies. Then, the calculated density of charged particles was so high in some quasars, that there was a problem of actually getting the photons, by which we see the objects, out from the interior. Then, very accurate positional measures by radio telescopes (very long base-line interferometry) revealed the astounding fact that some quasars appeared to be expanding with up to ten times the velocity of light. This was a flat-out violation of the known law of Einsteinian physics that the speed of light is a physical constant that cannot be exceeded in nature. Rather than move the quasars to lesser distances, which would give quite modest expansion velocities, the conventional theorists set up a small industry for rationalizations. They explained, by extremely complicated models, the faster-than-light expansions as an illusion caused by very special, assumed conditions such as ejection toward the observer at nearly the speed of light. They, of course, ignored the direct evidence that the quasars were associated with galaxies which were much closer to us in space.

When enough quasars were identified over the sky it became clear that anomalies also existed in the increase of their numbers with apparent faintness. For constant space density their numbers should have increased in proportion to the increased volumes enclosed at successively fainter apparent magnitudes. What was observed was completely different. This gave rise to another "gee whiz, isn't the universe wonderful" explanation. In this case, it was concluded that as we look out in space, and therefore back in time, we encounter a higher and higher density of quasars until suddenly—at a certain point—the quasars ceased to exist! In the present book, however, I do not debate whether this peculiar evolution of quasars is *a priori* improbable. I try to concentrate on the hard evidence of what they actually are and where they are located in space. In that process, we come again and again to observational evidence that redshift is not a good indicator of distances for quasars.

Now the debate takes a curious turn. The conventional wisdom says quasars are just abnormal galaxies (superluminous, etc.) and that galaxies can only have redshifts caused by velocity. I say yes. I, myself, pointed out originally that quasars are physically continuous with galaxies. *But* a large body of evidence now exists showing that *galaxies* also can violate the redshift-distance relation. In fact, it is just the most peculiar galaxies, those most like the quasars, for which the most compelling evidence for nonvelocity redshifts exists.

This has two consequences: First, it enormously strengthens the case that the redshift-distance law can be broken. After all, it only requires one well-proven, discordant case of quasar or galaxy to establish that an additional cause of redshift—other than velocity—must be in operation. Because of the connection of quasars with galaxies we now have many, interlocking proofs of the phenomenon.

But secondly it means that the mechanism for causing this nonvelocity shift must be capable of operating on an entire extended assemblage of stars, gas, and dust. This is much more difficult than finding a mechanism to operate on the more compact, more mysterious quasars.

The advance in understanding required to explain these observations has been thereby considerably escalated and now represents a spectacularly exciting challenge. The stakes in the theory game have been sharply raised.

The following book reflects the progression of evidence just discussed. The first five chapters deal with the anomalous evidence on quasars. The next three chapters deal with evidence for nonvelocity redshifts in galaxies. The final chapter combines this evidence and tries to explore the possible types of explanations which might account for the discordant data. Throughout the book, however, the reader will also be aware of many comments and anecdotes which bear on how the participants in the controversy have conducted the debate. The next-to-closing chapter deals with how I feel the acrimony arose in the debate and what it means for science.

One of the reasons for this commentary is that the reader needs to be aware that many professional astronomers do not believe that there is any need to change the conventional theory. Some accomplished and noted professionals do believe important, fundamental changes are necessary. A number are waiting to make up their mind—or see what others decide. But a number of astronomers vehemently reject the observations or the conclusions from them which are presented in this book. There are only two possibilities: One is that the conventional wisdom is right and that the observations are meaningless accidents. The other possibility is that the present thrust of the observations is correct and that some radical changes will have to be made in current theory.

This raises two questions for the reader: The first is, "What are the reasons which some astronomers give for disbelieving the evidence and conclusions of this book?" As to this question, I cannot possibly represent fairly the other side. Even if I could present it in an unbiased way, it would take an impossibly long time. The counterarguments to the evidence presented in this book, when they have been made in a few cases, are exceedingly complex and obscure and become hopelessly lost in technical detail. As Fred Hoyle has remarked, the establishment defends itself by "complicating everything to the point of incomprehensibility." I try to deal with valid, alternate possibilities as they arise, but the reader will either have to search out any original arguments from the references I give in the appendices to each chapter, or wait for a comprehensible rebuttal to this book to be published.

The second question raised is: "Assuming for the moment that the evidence in this book is correct, *why* have many professional astronomers disbelieved it?" That is an exceedingly important question because it bears on how human beings discover and gain knowledge and avoid harmful, entrenched mythologies. That is the reason I have included personal anecdote and commentary in this book. In case the thesis of this book is correct, we want to know what the factors are that led to this long, implacable rejection of new knowledge, the wasted effort, and the retardation of progress. Inevitably these factors involve emotional, personal, and ethical questions. These are explosive subjects down through the history of mankind. I am sure emotions will be stirred as a result of my comments in this book.

That I am willing to endure because I feel that the way in which research is conducted is one of the most crucial of mankind's activities. If the research is imaginative and accurate, and the human relations promote and protect this process, then the results will inevitably be worthwhile. If the process is biased, the practitioners too hostile or competitive for personal gain, or lacking in the crucial element of sportsmanship, then the results will inevitably be delayed and distorted.

The reader will have to make up his own mind on both questions, the correctness of the thesis of this book and also the validity of the comments on why some people tried to reject and suppress the results. Each reader will have to make up his own mind on these two questions, as in most important matters in life, on the basis of the evidence he has seen or heard.

DISTANCES 1
OF QUASARS

The following page shows a photograph of three quasars closely grouped around a large galaxy. The chance of these three quasars accidentally falling so close to a galaxy is between 10^{-5} and 10^{-7}, that is about one chance in a million. This is an enormously interesting observation because the quasars, with high redshifts, are conventionally supposed to be far behind, and unrelated to the galaxy which has a much lower redshift. Nevertheless, there was an attempt to suppress the discovery and observation of these quasars. When finally submitted to the *Astrophysical Journal*, publication was held up nearly $1\frac{1}{2}$ years. An anonymous referee stated, "The probability arguments are completely spurious."

What is the truth about this matter? Are the quasars related to the galaxy or not? And why the emotion, intrigues, and deadly professional combat which the subject has inspired for the last 20 years? To answer these questions, I believe, gives insight into the state of knowledge in astronomy today and also illuminates the passions, prejudices, and power relations in a modern science. We can explore the consequences of this for human

knowledge toward the end of this book, but first, let us just follow for a while the thread of one particular story, the history of the claimed association of quasars with galaxies.

In 1966 while checking galaxies in my newly completed *Atlas of Peculiar Galaxies*, I noticed that radio sources, including some quasars, fell close to, and aligned across, some of the particularly disturbed galaxies. Quasars had been just discovered in 1963 and already were being hailed as the most distant objects visible in the universe. If they were associated with relatively nearby galaxies, such as in the *Atlas*, however, they would themselves have to be relatively nearby. Some explanation for their high redshifts would have to be found other than expansion of the universe at large distances. In March 1966, I gave the evidence for these closer quasar distances in a colloquium at Caltech. I was told that one of the audience, later to become a vociferous opponent of the local hypothesis, had remarked in a characteristically loud and over-confident voice before the start of the conference, "Well, this will be the shot heard around the room." In contrast, after the colloquium, Fred Hoyle came up to the lectern

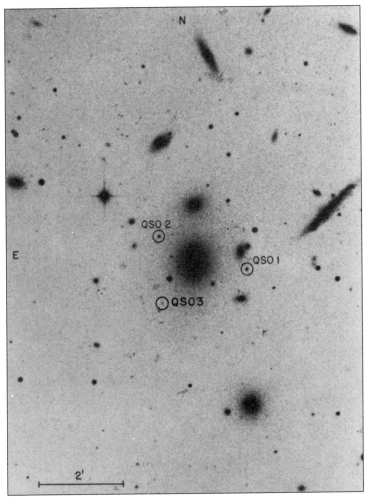

N

E

QSO 2

QSO 1

QSO3

2'

Figure 1-1. Three quasars close to the galaxy NGC 3842. The chances are about one in a million of finding this association accidentally.

and said, "Chip, we did not know about your results, but Geoffrey Burbidge and I have just submitted a paper which comes to the same conclusion, namely that quasars need not be the most distant objects, but could originate from nearby galaxies." But, in retrospect, it seems that the remark made that day, even before the observations were presented, signalled the implacable opposition of those who had accepted the original assumptions about quasars.

The first independent test of the newly found association between radio sources, quasars, and certain types of galaxies was published in *Nature* magazine in 1966 (see Appendix for reference). It concluded that the chance of obtaining the observed associations between peculiar galaxies and radio sources arranged randomly on the sky was about 1 in 100. But curiously, the authors took the standpoint that since the chance of being accidental was *only* 1 in 100, that there was no need to accept the significance of the association and test further the current assumptions. This attitude is distilled into the aphorism, "In order to make extraordinary changes in accepted scientific assumptions, one must have extraordinary observational evidence." Unfortunately, we will see that experience suggests that what this expression has come to mean in practice is: "In order to make basic changes in conventional assumptions, there is no evidence which is extraordinary enough".

Naturally, this last attitude cuts the very foundation from under science. It will be of great importance for us to see, in the following pages, whether the evidence really is strong enough, and if it is, whether extragalactic astronomy has a hope of once again becoming a science.

Quasars Associated with Galaxies

In the years since 1966 some few astronomers produced many investigations that purported to demonstrate the association of quasars with low-redshift galaxies at high levels of significance. A few papers appeared attacking these conclusions and much private opinion was circulated that the associations were meaningless accidents. The reaction of the rest of the field seems to have been not to ask which of this published evidence was correct, but only to fall back on mutually spoken reassurances that the association was not accepted. Among the parade of papers demonstrating association, however, one particularly startling result emerged in 1979, namely that there were three quasars projected near the edge of the spiral galaxy NGC 1073. This was the first example of *multiple* quasars very close to galaxies, which, of course, would be very much less likely to occur by chance than single quasars close to galaxies. Figure 1-2 shows this very beautiful barred spiral with the quasars measured by myself and Jack Sulentic marked by arrows. Ironically, the galaxy was originally photographed by Hubble in 1950, and is featured in the *Hubble Atlas of Galaxies*. This situation enabled me to make the pointed joke to my friend Allan Sandage, the author of that *Atlas*, and the co-discoverer of the first quasar, that his catalog of nearby galaxies seemed to contain many images of quasars well before they were discovered.

The probability that three quasars would be observed by chance so close to NGC 1073 is about 2×10^{-5} or about 1 chance in 50,000. But NGC 1073 appears so large and bright that it is one of only 176 galaxies in the *Hubble Atlas* and one of only 1246 galaxies in the *Shapley-Ames Catalog of Bright Galaxies*. Of course, the vast majority of these have never been searched for the presence of nearby quasars. It was only by curiosity after a small radio source was discovered near the galaxy that I looked for other quasars nearby and found a total of three close to NGC 1073. Therefore, the previous prediction that quasars fell close to nearby galaxies had been confirmed with an extremely high probability of significance by this system. Even if no more cases like this were found among bright galaxies, it would still be a significant confirmation of the hypothesis that some low redshift galaxies have associated quasars.

Usually in science one would expect an observation such as this to lead to the acceptance of the predicting hypothesis. In this case, the reality of the quasars was checked by some Caltech astronomers at Mt. Palomar Observatory, who refused to publish their confirmation and ignored the result. Confirmation was eventually published by the University of California astronomers E. Margaret Burbidge, V.T. Junkkarinen, and A.T. Koski. What the observation, and others like it, did lead to was a written warning from the allocation committee for Palomar telescope time threatening to cut my telescope time unless I refrained from such observations. In 1984, my observing time at Palomar was terminated.

But the quasars sit there, apparently in the outer arms of NGC 1073. From where did they originate? What can we learn about the nature of these mysteriously redshifted sources of energy if they indeed are intermingled in the filaments of gas and young stars in this spiral galaxy? The most direct way to answer these questions, as well as to confirm the reality of the physical association, was to find further examples of such associations.

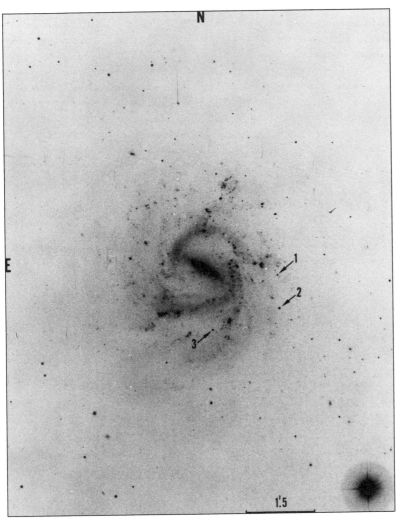

N

E

1.5

Figure 1-2. Three quasars near spiral arms of the galaxy NGC 1073. Quasars discovered by Arp and Sulentic.

It was helpful, therefore, when about the same time that the three quasars in the edge of NGC 1073 were being discovered, a pair of quasars turned up very close to the spiral galaxy NGC 622. The chance of finding two quasars this close to a galaxy is less than 4×10^{-4}, or less than 2×10^{-5} if one takes into account that the second quasar is quite bright. I discovered this system during the inspection of plates that registered ultraviolet objects over about 100 square degrees of sky. There should be from 10 to 50 galaxies as bright as NGC 622 in the region searched. Therefore, this was another very significant confirma-

tion. But the especially significant aspect of the NGC 622 configuration was a filament of material that came out of the galaxy and reached to the quasar, B1.

Quasars Ejected from Galaxies

This luminous connection is shown in Figure 1-3. It appears similar to a spiral arm of the galaxy except that it does not curve around as the edge of the galaxy does. Instead it comes straight out to end on what looks like an H II (gaseous emission) region. Right next to this knot is the quasar. The point is

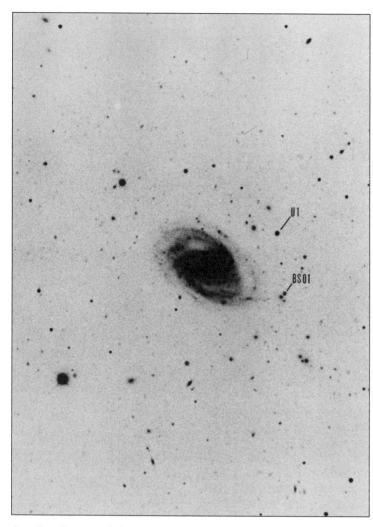

Figure 1-3. Two quasars improbably close to the galaxy NCG 622. The fainter, higher-redshift quasar B1 lies near the end of a straight filament emerging from the galaxy.

that the chances of this exceedingly unusual spiral arm ending almost exactly at the position of the quasar by accident is vanishingly small unless it is physically related. It also suggests ejection from the galaxy as the explanation for origin of the quasar. From the initial discovery of alignment of quasars across disturbed galaxies, the similarity to radio sources whose alignment is caused by ejection from the nucleus suggested an ejection origin for the quasars as well. The implication has always been that the quasars are ejected from the nucleus of the associated galaxy. We will see in coming chapters continuing and inter-

locking evidence for ejection of material from galaxies. Second only to the question of origin of nonvelocity redshift, the ejection of material seems to be the most significant puzzle related to galaxies. Ejection from the nuclei of active galaxies raises the question of whether conditions in that innermost center involve the normal terrestrial physics that we know about. Could the strangeness of quasars be related to the very different nature of their material if they originated in active galactic nuclei?

The quasar/galaxy associations shown in Figures 1-2 and 1-3 of the preceding pages

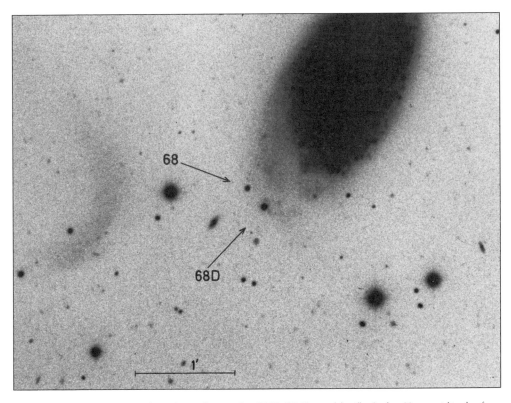

Figure 1-4. Two quasars are seen projected very close together near edge of NGC 470. Photograph by Allan Sandage. Note material in edge of galaxy apparently associated with quasars.

were announced at the Texas Symposium on Relativistic Astrophysics in Munich in December 1978. This review paper presented evidence from systematic searches around a few dozen galaxies in selected regions of the sky. It was shown that a number of companion galaxies to spirals (apparently the most active kinds of galaxies) had single quasars close by to them with a probability of chance association, for the whole sample of only 10^{-6} to 10^{-14}. This was, of course, in *addition* to the highly significant confirmation of multiple quasars associated with galaxies which was already discussed here in relation to Figures 1-2 and 1-3.

Most of the participants in the Texas Symposium were impressed by the results. But riding back to the hotel in the bus, I recall that in the deep seats immediately in front of me were Walter Sullivan, science writer for

the *New York Times* and the most prominent quasar researcher of the day. The latter was explaining to Sullivan, with great patience and kindness, how all the apparent associations were accidental and how the quasars could not be local. To the credit of Sullivan, the stories on the associations did appear in the *Times* and similar evidence was also later reported in the *Times* over the years. But, the quietly spoken opinion of the astronomical authority was to prevail over the published evidence within his inner circle of science.

The sharp and lethal battle which came in 1983 about the statistics of quasars near galaxies will be the subject of the next chapter. But first let us bring the story of multiple quasar associations up to date by reporting a more recent discovery. This is shown in Figure 1-4. The bright, spiral galaxy from the

Shapley-Ames Catalog of Bright Galaxies, NGC 470, is shown to have two newly discovered quasars in the edge of its disk. The probability of finding two quasars like the fainter one this close to a given point in the sky is about 2 x 10^{-4}. Since one quasar is considerably brighter, and therefore less common, the probability of finding the actual quasars is even smaller. This discovery comes from an area in which about five galaxies this bright were present. Therefore, the total probability of finding this configuration by accident in that investigation was less than one in a thousand.

It is interesting to note how my collaborators in this discovery computed the probability. Putting forward the hypothesis that this is what drew attention to the galaxy, they began by pretending the first quasar did not exist. Then they asked, what is the probability of finding only the second quasar this close to a galaxy? Since this probability is still quite small, they said, well, let's move it further away from the galaxy where it would still attract our attention but where it would be more probable to encounter by accident. They still obtained a significant improbability for their modified configuration but, of course, much less than the improbability of the actual association. I am quite pleased that they were willing to publish their computation in our paper because I think it furnishes a surprisingly vivid record of how, when astronomers of conventional belief have a choice between two possibilities, the more bias toward the current assumption they make, the more proper they feel the calculation is.

Of course, the latest discovery is the strikingly close arrangement of three quasars around the galaxy shown in Figure 1-1. This object will be discussed further in later chapters.

Table 1-1 summarizes the properties of those four systems in which we, so far, have

TABLE 1-1
Galaxies With Multiple Quasars

GALAXY		QUASAR				
Name	Redshift	Name	Dist. (arcsec)	Mag.	Red Shift	Probability
NGC 622	0.018	UB1	71	18.5	0.91	0.001
		BSO1	73	20.2	1.46	0.02
NGC 470	0.009	68	95	19.9	1.88	0.015
		68D	95	18.2	1.53	0.002
NGC 1073	0.004	BSO1	104	19.8	1.94	0.01
		BSO2	117	18.9	0.60	0.006
		RSO	84	20.0	1.40	0.02
NGC 3842	0.020	QSO1	73	19.0	0.34	0.003
		QSO2	59	19.0	0.95	0.002
		QSO3	73	21.0	2.20	0.01

found galaxies with multiple, apparently associated quasars. An estimate of the improbability of chance occurrence is given for each quasar. It is noticeable that the quasars have a tendency to be fainter for larger redshift. This will be discussed in later chapters where evidence is advanced that the high-redshift quasars ($z=2$) have the lowest intrinsic luminosity. It is also noticeable in Table 1-1 that certain preferred redshift values appear more frequently than one would expect by chance.

Preferred Values of Redshift

This observed property of quasars having certain preferred redshifts has an extraordinary history and followed a typical course in the field. Geoffrey Burbidge noticed early in the measurements of quasar redshifts that too many redshifts occurred too close to the value $z=1.95$. He argued vigorously for the reality of the effect but others put emphasis on the quasars of other redshifts which were observed and ridiculed the effect. There was a sort of heroic underground of analysis of quasar periodicities starting with Burbidge and Burbidge in 1967 and continued by a number of astronomers, particularly Karlsson in 1971, 1973, and 1977, Barnothy and Barnothy in 1976, and Depaquit, Pecker, and Vigier in 1984. They all more or less agreed if you looked at all quasars known, that preferred values of redshift were apparent.

In the latest and most complete analysis those preferred values of redshift were:

TABLE 1-2

z (ALL QUASARS)	z (NGC 1083)
0.30	
0.60	0.60
0.96	
1.41	1.40
1.96	1.94

As the small table above shows, the redshifts of the quasars belonging to NGC 1073 (Figure 1-2) average only 0.01 from three of the magic values. This is like a key fitting into a lock. But, of course, what is behind that locked door is terrifying to conventional astronomy.

The three quasars around NGC 3842 (Figure 1-1) fit a pattern of slightly different periodicity, a period characteristic of a different group of quasars. These slight differences in period interval between groups of quasars confirm the main periodicity and at the same time confirm that each individual association of quasars is a physically related group in spite of their being composed of different redshifts. This result will be analyzed further in Chapter 5, where evidence for the reality of different groups of quasars in different regions of space will be presented. References and further comments on the past analyses of periodicities in redshifts of quasars are given at the end of the Appendix to this chapter.

Summary

To summarize this initial chapter, I would emphasize that with the known densities with which quasars of different apparent brightness are distributed over the sky, one can compute what are the chances of finding by accident a quasar at a certain distance from a galaxy (see Appendix to this chapter). When this probability is low, finding a second or third quasar within this distance is the product of these two or three improbabilities, or very much lower. It is perhaps difficult to appreciate immediately just how unlikely it is to encounter quasars this close by chance, but when galaxies with two or three quasars as close as we have shown here are encountered, one needs only a few cases to establish beyond doubt that the associations cannot be accidental.

We should also note that the hypothesis that quasars fall closer to galaxies than would be expected by chance was made and demonstrated by the available evidence in 1966. Long before the writing of this book a number of investigations had confirmed this association. But the present chapter, which presents the latest evidence on just the multiple quasar associations alone, confirms with overwhelming significance the fact of the associations.

The vast majority of galaxies remain to be investigated. It is clear that many of these will yield additional confirmations and give further valuable data on the properties of the quasars which would help us understand the real nature of their redshifts. The last few observational programs of this kind have now been blocked by the committees which have been appointed by most observatory directors to allocate telescope time. It is with a considerable sense of relief, however, that I can say that I think the observations have been suppressed too late. As I hope we can continue to demonstrate in this book—the observational proof of this extremely important phenomenon has already been gathered.

Appendix to Chapter 1—Probabilitites of Associations

The basic quantity needed to compute the probability of a quasar falling within any given distance from a point on the sky is just the average density of that kind of quasar per unit area on the sky. For example, if a quasar of 20th apparent magnitude falls 60 arcsec away from a galaxy, we simply say that within this radius of a galaxy there is a circular area of 0.0009 square degrees. The average density of quasars from the brightest down to 20th apparent magnitude is about 6 to 10 per square degree. Therefore, the most generous probability, on average, for finding one of these quasars in our small circle is about 0.001 x 10 = 0.01, that is, a chance of about one in a hundred.

The crucial quantity is the observed average density. The comparison of what various observers have measured for this quantity is given in Arp 1983, page 504 (see following list of references). Overall, the various densities measured agree fairly well, certainly to within ± 40%. For the kinds of quasars considered in these first few chapters this gives probabilities that cannot be significantly questioned. Of course, on the cosmological assumption, quasars of various redshifts must project on the sky rather uniformly. Therefore adherents of this viewpoint cannot object to taking an average background density, as observed, to compute probabilities of chance occurrences.

Although quite smooth enough to compute average probabilities of association as done in the previous chapter, the cosmological assumption of uniform quasar background has led to some consternation for certain other kinds of quasars discussed in later chapters.

Typically one astronomer will measure one kind of quasar in one direction and get either a large or small difference from previous measures. He will then argue that his measure is "the" correct answer and other observers were in error. He will seldom consider that the differences are real. This has led to some considerable gymnastics to try to avoid inhomogeneities of certain kinds of quasars in certain regions. A good example of this is in the 1981 reference below, which tries to rationalize a difference of more than a factor of 10 in bright apparent magnitude, high-redshift quasars in one direction in the sky. In another instance, noted below, differences in densities are dismissed as scale errors when in fact they are due to the use of continuum magnitude systems that exclude emission lines, being incorrectly compared to broad-band systems that include them.

Some references which will amplify subjects discussed in this chapter are listed below with some comments.

1967, Arp, H., Astrophysical Journal, 148, p. 321.
This is the first detailed paper discussing associations between radio sources and peculiar galaxies.

1966, Lynden-Bell, D., Cannon, R. D., Penston, M. V., and Rothman, V. C. A., Nature. 211, p. 838.
First tests of the above associations.

1968, van der Laan, H., and Bash, F. N., Astrophysical Journal, 152, p. 621.
1968, Arp, H., Astrophysical Journal, 152, p. 633. ·
First paper critical of the associations and reply by Arp.

1973, "The Redshift Controversy," ed. G. Field, W. A. Benjamin, Inc., Reading, Mass.
Three points not widely known about this, a report of the only actual debate to take place on the subject, are: (1) I tried to challenge the best-known quasar experts in the field at that time but none would accept; (2) after the debate had

been arranged, the director of my observatory heard that it was going to take place and telephoned to try to stop it; (3) the profits from the sale of the book went to support the work of Section D, the astronomy section of the AAAS (American Association for the Advancement of Science) before which the debate was held. The book summarizes and discusses the main developments before 1972.

1979, Arp. H. and Sulentic, J. W., Astrophys. Journal, 229, p. 496.

This is the report of the three quasars closely spaced around the galaxy NGC 1073 (Fig. 1-2 here).

1980, Arp H., Annals of the New York Academy of Sciences, 336, p. 94.

This is a review paper given at the Ninth Texas Symposium on Relativistic Astrophysics held in Munich in Dec. 1978. The paper summarizes the associations of quasars and galaxies to that date, reports the associations with NGC 622 and NGC 1073, and introduces the associations of quasars with the famous disturbed or exploding galaxy, M82.

1981, Smith, M.G., "Investigating the Universe," ed. F. D. Kahn, D. Reidel Publishing Co., Dordrecht, Holland p. 151.

This article attempts to rationalize order-of-magnitude discrepancies in quasar densities in different directions and backward running Hubble relations as "selection effects." See articles below:

1983, Arp, H., Nature, 302, p. 397.
1984, Arp, H., Astrophys. Journal, 285, p. 555.

These two articles discuss the evidence against excusing quasar groupings and redshift-apparent magnitude anomalies as selection effects.

1982, Veron, P. and Veron, M. P., Astron. and Astrophys., 105, p. 405.

This paper dismisses discrepancies in quasar densities in different directions as "due to errors in magnitude scales used." The paper below shows it failed to distinguish between continuum and broad-band magnitudes.

1983, Arp. H., Astrophys. Journal, 271, p. 479.

On page 504 of this article the density of quasars on the sky is discussed, comparisons are made to values measured by various observers, and different magnitude systems are discussed.

1984, Arp. H. and Gavazzi, G., Astron. and Astrophys., 139, p.240.

Discussion of three quasars newly discovered around NGC 3842 as shown in this chapter in Figure 1-1 and Table 1.

1984, Arp, H., Surdej, J., and Swings, J. P., Astron. and Astrophys., 138, p. 179.

Discussion of two newly discovered quasars at the edge of NGC 470 as shown in this chapter in Figure 1-4 and Table 1.

Periodicities in the observed quasar redshifts have been analyzed by a number of authors. The latest references, from which the earlier references may be gleaned are:

1984, Depaquit, S., Pecker, J.-C., and Vigier, J.-P., Astronomische Nachrichten, 305. p. 339.
1984, Box, T. C. and Roeder. R. C., Astronomy and Astrophysics, 134, p. 234.

Note on Periodicities in Quasar Redshifts.

Periodicities in quasar redshifts have been found in all samples except one where the person who analyzed it truncated the sample in a particular way that removed the periodicities (see Depaquit *et al.* reference). Some authors have argued selection effects are responsible for the periodicities. This is clearly untrue because major emission lines can be seen with objective prism searches throughout the redshift range. Concentrations of redshifts close to $z = 1$ for optically selected quasars around companion galaxies and in dense groups of quasars prove that techniques of photographic discovery by ultraviolet excess are not significantly biased. Of course, quasars selected by their radio emission should not be biased in redshift at all. It is shown in Chapter 5 that all quasars tend to have certain rather discrete, permitted redshifts but that different groups have slightly different periods. It is the addition of these slightly shifted peaks from group to group which broadens the overall peaks as observed in the total quasar sample. The bottom line is that quasars have the astonishing property of occurring at certain preferred values of redshift, these values occurring with a definite period whose origin is a mystery at this moment.

The crucial discovery of periodicities in quasar redshifts was made by K. G. Karlsson. That discovery was that the redshift peaks fit a formula $\Delta \log (1 + z) = $ const. As Table 2 in the preceding text shows, the observed redshift peaks for the average of all quasars fit the formula with const. = 0.089. Individual physical groups of quasars have slightly different constants (see Arp, review paper presented at *IAU* Symposium 124, Beijing, China, August 1986). Unfortunately, a possibility of which all young astronomers are aware occurred in the Karlsson case. This creative researcher was not employed in astronomy and subsequently went into medical science.

THE BATTLE 2
OVER STATISTICS

As mentioned in the first chapter, after 1966, a number of investigations built up the evidence that quasars were associated with nearby galaxies. One of the first systematic investigations of quasars over the sky was an analysis I published in 1970. I was still a faculty member at Caltech at the time, and I remember well the custom of astronomy luncheons at the Faculty Club every Friday. I would bring in new examples of quasars falling improbably close to galaxies and share these photographs with my colleagues. Finally, the consensus was communicated to me that they believed these to be specially selected cases and that as scientists they could only accept the effect if a full statistical test were performed on a complete sample. I thereupon took about six months away from normal activities, enlisted the aid of Fritz Bartlett, a radio astronomer, to program the large IBM computer which Caltech then relied upon, and proceeded to analyze the position of all the then-known 3CR quasars *(Third Cambridge Catalog Revised Survey of Strong Radio Sources)* with respect to all the galaxies listed in the *Shapley-Ames Catalog of Bright Galaxies.*

Figure 2-1 shows the striking result of those computations. It shows how the separations on the sky between a set of radio quasars and cataloged galaxies steadily decreases as brighter and brighter galaxies are considered—that is, the association with these quasars is stronger as galaxies closer to us in space are considered. The powerful computer enabled many imaginary sets of random quasars to be generated and compared to the galaxies, and thus showed that it was only the real quasars which had this property of falling closer and closer to brighter and brighter galaxies.

I returned with excitement and anticipation to the Friday luncheon and explained what I had found out. There was a unanimous response:

"Oh, no one believes statistics!"

The paper containing these results was published in 1970 in the *Astronomical Journal* and little notice was taken of it. Eventually, in 1983, I utilized some of the clues developed in that paper to make the most recent and detailed proposals as to the location of quasars in space. These concepts are developed further in Chapter 5.

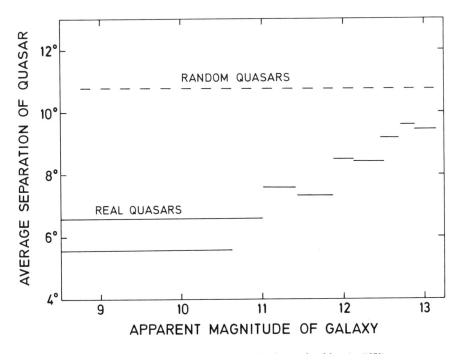

Figure 2-1. The mean separation of a set of radio emitting quasars from very bright galaxies. Adapted from Arp (1970).

But, other investigators were also developing evidence that quasars were associated with galaxies on the sky. In 1971, G. R. Burbidge, E. M. Burbidge, P. M. Solomon, and P. A. Strittmatter showed that among the quasars then known, those that fell very close on the sky to bright galaxies fell much closer than would be expected by chance. In a carefully worked-out statistical analysis, they showed that with even the few cases known from casual investigation, the chance that these closest coincidences occurred accidentally was less than 5×10^{-3} or of the order of one in two hundred.

The result was never criticized in print. As usual, however, it was excoriated in private. One of the major techniques for dismissing such results was introduced about this time. The catch-phrase is known as "a posteriori statistics." Normal people may not find that so catchy. But the idea is rather simple: After any event has happened, the probability of it happening in that precise way can al-

ways be computed to be vanishingly small. For example, if two people are photographed in the streets of a city of one million inhabitants, we would say that the chance of A being directly adjacent to B is one in a million. But in any random street scene there are perforce many A's next to unrelated B's. This is all quite evident from common sense. But what is also quite evident from common sense is, that if we continue to get photographs at different times and places of A next to B, we had better conclude some relationship exists between A and B. So far as the charge of "a posteriori statistics" which has been levelled at each new piece of quasar evidence is concerned, the association of quasars with galaxies was demonstrated in 1966. Each succeeding example has therefore been an additional confirmation of an "a priori" prediction. The dismissal of each of these on a case-by-case basis with the excuse of "posteriori statistics" has been, at best, poor science and, at worst, a tactic of evasion.

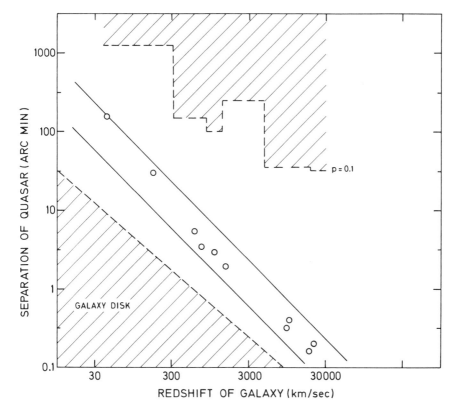

Figure 2-2. Relation showing that the greater the distance of the galaxy from the observer, the smaller is the apparent separation of the associated quasar. From Arp (1983).

G. R. Burbidge, S. L. O'Dell, and P. A. Strittmatter in a later paper in 1972 showed that quasars associated with more remote galaxies appeared closer to the galaxy of association, as if the whole partnership was viewed from a greater distance. This relation is very important because it is what we must expect if we view associations through a range of distances, some associations close by and some more distant. The relation was later strongly confirmed over a much larger range in distance of the central galaxy and with larger numbers of examples in a paper by Arp in 1983. This is shown here in Figure 2-2.

At first sight this result seems to contradict the previous result that quasars fall closer to brighter, more nearby galaxies. The key point to understand, however, is that nearby quasars are statistically close (closer, on the average, than one would expect by chance) to nearby galaxies and that more distant quasars are statistically close to more distant galaxies. But, the nearby associations can subtend a large angle on the sky and have rather large separations compared to the separations involved in more distant associations. The difficulty comes when people assume on the local hypothesis (quasars closer than their redshift distances) that all quasars are at the *same* distance and then try to analyze this mixture of quasars at different distances with galaxies at different distances. Naturally they get porridge. An example of this follows.

In 1980, a test analysis was made by one researcher of some quasars which had been found in sample areas of the sky by objective prism techniques. (The objective prism on a telescope enables the selection of objects which have strong emission lines in their spectrum—the stellar images among these are mostly quasars.) These objective prism quasars were analyzed to see how close on the sky they fell to NGC galaxies. (Perhaps indicative of the fast pace at which astronomy moves, the *New General Catalog of Galaxies* (*NGC*) by Caroline and William Herschel was completed by J. L. E. Dreyer in 1888.) The NGC contains over 7000 objects, most of which are fainter objects at medium to large distances. There are no accurate magnitude limits for this *Catalog* and in addition an inhomogeneous selection of objects was made. But the Arp paper in 1970 showed bright quasars to be generally associated with the brightest galaxies in the sky. Why did the later paper in 1980 try to associate quasars with more distant galaxies?

And, should it have been such a surprise when it reported no significant associations? Perhaps there is some clue to be had in reading carefully the words of the author as he coyly "suggests" that the "seemingly high frequency of quasar/galaxy pairs reported, primarily by Arp" may be due to "uncertainties" in the adopted quasar densities used and "it is this effect that makes many astronomers skeptical about the statistical significance of Arp's configurations."

The true state of affairs was illuminated a year later by the only young astronomer to have ever regularly dared to test the claims of the establishment. Jack Sulentic analyzed the quasars just discussed as having been claimed to disprove association with galaxies. He analyzed these same quasars and also additional samples, but this time with respect to the bright nearby galaxies with which they were supposed to be associated. He found consistent and significant quasar/galaxy associations in all the quasar samples! Moreover, he found the quasars associated with fainter galaxies fell closer to them on the sky as would be expected if these fainter galaxies were more distant.

All this poses an interesting question: Why, when the establishment believes so fiercely in the different distances of galaxies (as indicated by their different redshifts), do they always insist on testing the association of galaxies and quasars by assuming that all galaxies (bright and faint) are at the same distance from us?

We will see this obviously incorrect assumption used again and again in attempts to disprove the association of quasars and galaxies.

A. Quasars near Companion Galaxies

During these investigations of quasars associated with galaxies, it became apparent that a particularly favorable configuration existed when a large spiral had an associated companion galaxy. Strikingly closer to these companions than expected by chance were found quasars.

A representative selection of the cases is shown in Figure 2-3. One reason for this could be that the companion galaxies are younger and more active and tend to produce more quasars. But whatever the explanation may be, the associations furnish vivid evidence of quasars associated with much lower redshift galaxies.

As this evidence built up, the opposition became more silent. I felt that one final test would enable a resolution of the question. Starting in 1978, I outlined a considerable section of the sky, defined beforehand what kinds of galaxies I was looking for quasars around, and started to make the observations. (The area of the sky sampled was defined by bright spirals with companions that were contained between the right ascensions of NGC 2460 and 3184.) For long nights on the Mt. Palomar 48-inch Schmidt telescope I photographed these areas in the sky in two colors in such a way as to be able to pick out the ultraviolet-excess, stellar-appearing objects which were the quasar candidates. I laboriously scanned the plates for the candidates and struggled with the spectrograph on the 200-inch Mt. Palomar reflector to obtain their individual spectra so that I might know with certainty which were *bona fide* quasars.

Finally, after three years, I had finished. From 34 predefined candidate galaxies, I had found 13 cases where the quasars fell so close that the chances were, *in each individual case*, only about 1 in 100 of being accidentally associated. To find 13 such cases out of a limited number of trials implied fantastic odds against being a chance occurrence. I calculated about 10^{-17} (one chance in a billion would be 10^{-9})

The result was published in the *Astrophysical Journal*. A month or so passed. Suddenly the storm broke. Two papers arrived, each denouncing the probability calculations. They had been sent to the *Astrophysical Journal Letters* for quick publication and copies had been sent on to me by the Journal as a customary notification of critical papers. Both papers took essentially the same tack, that because I had used a probability of about one in a hundred of being accidental as a criterion for being associated, all cases where the probability was even slightly greater should be excluded. They wound up in the ludicrous position that associations where the probability was 0.012 or 0.013 should be excluded from the calculation as not improbable. (Basing my original probablilty calculation on p $\le$ 0.015, instead of the rounded-off p $\sim$ 0.01 I used, would have raised my final probability of accidental association from p $\sim 10^{-17}$ to p $= 7 \times 10^{-16}$). These papers also used scaled densities of faint quasars to calculate the probabilities of finding bright quasars, despite the fact that it was clear from the literature that these brighter quasars were much less common. They also assumed that areas had been searched for quasars that had not been searched. These papers, after extensive refereeing, were never published. What did the damage was a paper that used the same in-

correct arguments which was published with extreme rapidity by a British journal, *Monthly Notices of the Royal Astronomical Society*.

I first became aware of this paper when I received an unprecedented note from the editor of the main *Astrophysical Journal*. (The main Journal has a separate editor from the Letters section.) He mailed me a preprint of the paper which was to appear so quickly thereafter in the *Monthly Notices*. The note from the *Ap. J.* editor read essentially:

"We received this from the author and are conveying this simply for your information."

Professional ethics required that both the author and the *Monthly Notices* send this kind of preprint directly to me. But, since from that day forward, my papers had enormous difficulties appearing in the *Astrophysical Journal*, I eventually understood what was the probable reason for this highly unusual maneuver.

There was a further effect of the *Monthly Notices* paper, however, which presented me with additional problems. Another astronomer from the British establishment, who had been in communication with the first, sent a note to the *Astrophysical Journal Letters* which was eventually published. It took a different, apparently more valid tack. It pointed out that when I computed the probability of finding a quasar of a certain brightness at a certain distance from a galaxy, that I should also take into account that I could find other quasars at different brightnesses and distances that could also have a low probability of chance occurrence. In other words, there was more than one way of obtaining a chance-occurrence probablility of about 1 in 100. That gave me a number of sleepless nights because I had to acknowledge that this appeared to be a flaw in my original thinking.

After pondering the question deeply, I finally came to the conclusion that I had intuitively assumed that galaxies at a certain distance would possess quasars at a certain,

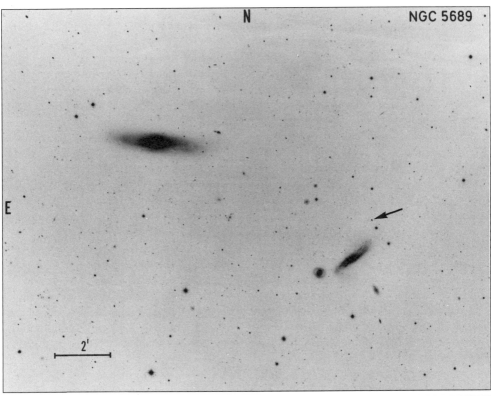

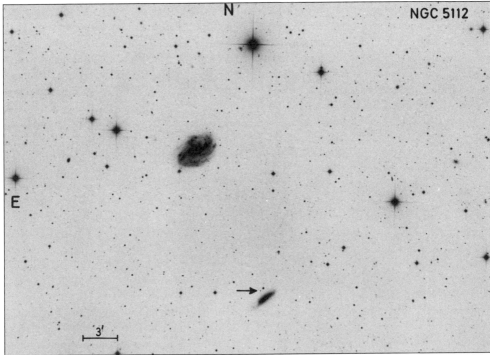

Figure 2-3. A representative set of examples of large spirals that have companion galaxies with apparently associated quasars. The arrows mark the quasars. See also NGC 5296/97 in following chapter (Fig. 3-6). None of these examples were used in the complete statistical analysis of the test area discussed in the text and shown in Figs. 2-4 through 2-6.

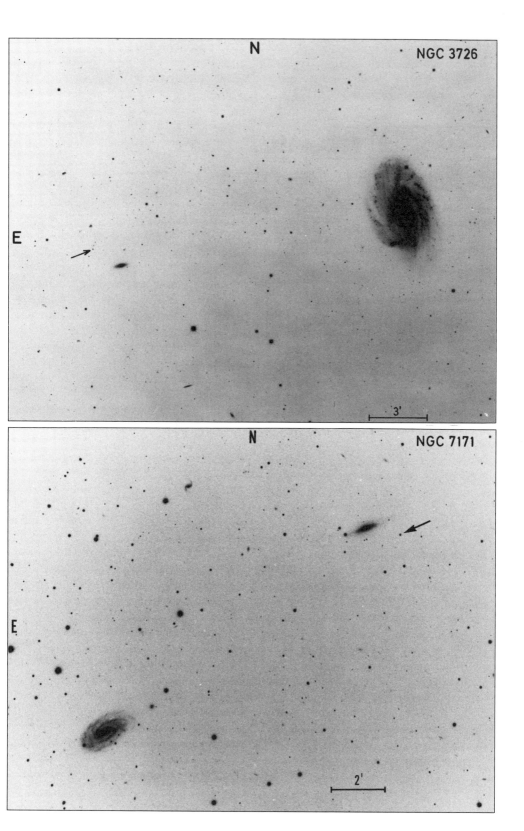

N

NGC 3726

E

3'

N

NGC 7171

E

2'

characteristic separation from the galaxy and that other separations would not occur. Actually, this is just the relation shown in Figure 2-2. With considerable anxiety, I recalculated the probabilities in a completely different manner, taking into account explicitly instead of implicitly the distance of the central galaxy calculated from the conventional redshift criterion of its distance. I got the same improbability of association. I felt vastly relieved that my initial assumption had been correct.

I encouraged publication of the paper that criticized this aspect of my previous probability calculation and accompanied it with a recalculation, by the different method, which confirmed my original results. Actually, the critical paper, even after making the most unrealistic and unfavorable assumptions, still derived an improbability of 10^{-7} that the original result could be accidental. This was still enormously strong confirmation of my original result. But the whole point of that paper was suddenly contradicted by a note added in proof (unseen by me or any referee) that referred to the *Monthly Notices* paper as disproving my original result. So the whole scientific content of the exchange was defeated. Reading now the papers, from some distance in time, it is clear that this was a rather effective double-play between two authors. In order to eliminate what seemed to be the inescapably small probability of chance occurrence originally obtained, one claimed that part was due to a large factor of error due to one cause and the other a large factor of error from another cause—neither had to make a formal calculation from the actual data.

An extensive recalculation on these data was later made by two other authors, E. J. Zuiderwijk and H. R. de Ruiter. It was reported in the *Monthly Notices* 1983 (see Appendix). With essentially the same precepts as the earlier authors, they found instead an association of quasars with the galaxies with an overall chance of only about 1 in 100 of being accidental. The reason that this still fell short of my original improbability is that they also ignored the fact that the galaxies with which the quasars are associated have varying distances from us. The absolutely key point is that my original calculation used a simple way of taking into account the different distances from us of the galaxies around which the quasars were found. To ignore this elementary piece of astronomy in which everyone believes leads to a strong dilution of the effect by looking in areas where quasars are not expected to be found and ignoring areas where they are. The nub of the matter is the following: When testing the null hypothesis, the assumption that the quasars *are not* associated, the last two authors find evidence for association. The burning question then becomes, why not test the hypothesis that they *are* associated, taking into account the varying distance of the galaxies? Why not repeat the test which gave the original, overwhelmingly significant association with the galaxies?

Of course, when two sides differ so sharply over calculations performed on the same data, one side must be wrong. If my side is wrong, I have to wonder whether I got the wrong answer because I wanted very much a certain result and this desire prejudiced my judgment on how to make the calculation. The other side would have to face the same question. Perhaps this is what is preventing the calculation from being pressed to the decision that it is certainly capable of.

Finally, in 1983, a paper by myself was published in the *Astrophysical Journal* giving the final data on the observed fields and reanalyzing the statistics. Figure 2-4 here is from that paper and shows how the quasars concentrate between about 7 to 20 kpc radius around the particular galaxies that were sampled in that investigation. The average background density of quasars could not conceivably contribute significantly to the

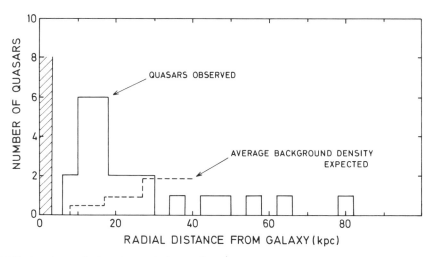

Figure 2-4. Numbers of quasars found as a function of radius around companion galaxies in Arp's 1983 study. Expected average background counts are shown by the dashed line.

observed numbers in the small area on the sky in which these quasars were found. In fact, the density of quasars at these radial distances from their associated galaxies (in this investigation the investigated galaxies were all companion galaxies to larger galaxies) exceeded by more than 20 times the measured density of these kinds of quasars away from such galaxies. This result appears in Figure 2-5, where the error bars on the determinations from quasars of various apparent brightness class are also shown. All three magnitude classes of quasars agree that the excess density around these galaxies must be, taking a liberal estimate of the possible background density of quasars, between 10 and 30 times that background density. This is the same result that was the conclusion of the first, much maligned paper. Apparently the chance of accidentally getting an overdensity by the original factor of 20 is about 10^{-17} (or more accurately, 7×10^{-16}).

The final published data and exhaustive analysis, however, made no difference. It was sufficient for many astronomers to have something—anything—in print claiming the associations were spurious. This was brought home with particular vividness after a physics-astronomy conference in Geneva in

November 1983. I was chatting with a British cosmologist about C fields and inflationary theory when the subject of quasars was mentioned. This theorist looked distressed and said apologetically: "Well, I was interested in your quasar investigations, but then I was told your observational evidence had been proved wrong."

It was clear that the research had been successfully discredited.

But, before that I was even more painfully aware that the event had been used with disastrous effect within my own home observatory. While the critical paper that had been published so quickly in the *Monthly Notices* was still in preprint form, it had also been sent, special communication to the new director of my observatory, courtesy of the most eminent quasar researcher on the Caltech faculty. This occurred shortly after Caltech had broken the agreement to jointly operate Palomar Observatory with Carnegie Institution of Washington.

Soon after this, a friend of mine met the director at the airport in Washington, D.C., and asked about me. The answer came back:

"Well, I wish he would get his statistics right!"

When I heard this, I went to his office

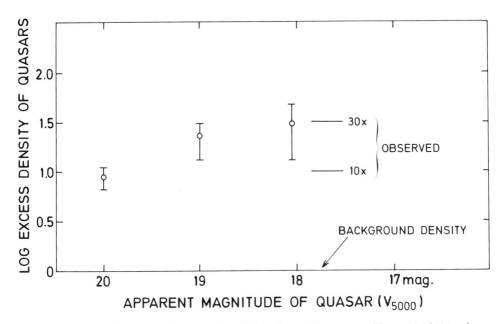

Figure 2-5. *The excess density of quasars around companion galaxies. Bright, medium, and faint quasars are all between 10 and 30 times denser than in the average field.*

and put down on his desk a copy of my final paper in which I had recalculated all the statistics using a different method and verified the original answer. Weeks later, in a talk with him, however, he spoke angrily about ludicrous arguments on my part and finally said, in effect:

"No matter what you do, you will never be able to prove that you are right. If you are right it will have to proved by someone else."

Afterwards, I reflected that this was truly a serious crisis when a scientist admitted that he could not be convinced by any possible scientific evidence, and moreover, that personal prejudices played a part in judging the experimental evidence.

Of course an infallible method exists for even highly placed scientists to get into big trouble—that is simply to get the "wrong" answer. This was vividly demonstrated, aside from the papers referenced earlier in this chapter which supported the associations, by the case of the then director of the Kitt Peak National Observatory, G. R. Burbidge. Together with some collaborators, he had sub-

mitted a statistical analysis on this subject. The study utilized the extremely valuable, complete catalog of all known quasars that had by then been compiled in collaboration with Del Hewitt. The sophisticated statistical analysis showed again strong evidence for correlation of quasars with bright galaxies. The referee's report on this paper excited wonderment in all those who gazed at it. As is all too common these days, the anonymous referee utilized trivial criticisms and inapplicable arguments against the paper. Since there was no sign of this obvious blocking coming to an end, or any intervention by the editor, it was sent to another journal. That journal sent it to another astronomer, who prides himself on his scientific intransigence, and it was rejected out of hand. Would the paper ever appear or would it become a rare, suppressed collector's item? Happily, it was finally published in 1984 in *Astronomy and Astrophysics*, another strong confirmation of the association of quasars with relatively nearby galaxies.

Perhaps an equally vivid demonstration of how the publication of scientific results can

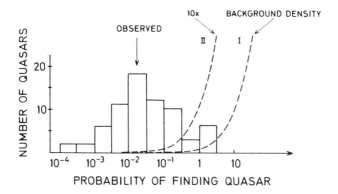

Figure 2-6. *The improbability of quasar associations with companion galaxies plotted against the number observed. Expected relations for observed random background (I) and ten times density of observed background (II). From DuBois, Giraud, and Vigier (1983).*

be hampered is the case of a paper by the creative and knowledgeable French physicist, Jean-Pierre Vigier, and two collaborators. Seeing the attack on the statistics of the association of quasars near companion galaxies, they carried out an analysis of their own. Figure 2-6 above shows that they made yet another, but very elegant approach to the problem. They plotted the number of quasars found near companions as a function of the improbability of finding them. Then, as Figure 2-6 shows, they calculated the expected probability of such proximity if the quasars were distributed randomly with respect to the galaxies. The figure shows that even if the background density were an order of magnitude (ten times) greater than the value it is actually measured to be, the quasars still, very obviously, fell much closer to the galaxies than could be explained by chance. The fate of this paper did not involve much suspense. It was rejected without hesitation by the same journal that published the original, supposed refutation. This confirmatory paper wound up being published in the *Comptes Rendus de l'Academie des Sciences Paris*. A noble publication in the past, *Comptes Rendus*, with papers like this, might have to become more regular reading for those few astronomers who wish to know "how it really is."

Perhaps none of these occurrences would be any more serious than confrontations between opinions in science and human affairs of the kind that have taken place many times in the past. What has happened in astronomy today, however, is that almost all telescope access has been shut off to the proponents of one point of view—namely the point of view that current assumptions should be subject to observational test and that contradictory and surprising evidence should be followed up. The irony is that previously no more than about 5 percent of telescope time was given to projects that explored outside of the conventional, run-of-the-mill beliefs. To add this 5 percent additional time to the routine programs makes no significant contribution to them; it merely has the effect of suppressing all the discovery-mode programs. In a way, it is testimony to the extreme fear that the opposing side has of this kind of research that they would ruthlessly seek out and subdue this small effort. On the other hand, it raises the question of whether the enormous financial, engineering, and administrative effort put into astronomical research today is being wasted at the point of application by scientists who believe they already know all the important answers.

Appendix to Chapter 2

There are many references to the events described in this chapter. Some of the main papers are referenced below and the remaining references can be gleaned from a reading of these papers:

1970, Arp, H., Astron. Journ., 75, p. 1.

This is the first paper testing the association of real quasars with bright galaxies versus randomly generated sets of quasars. The line of quasars near NGC 520 and differences in quasars between the direction of the center of the Local Group of galaxies and the supergalactic center are first introduced. The latter subjects will be amplified in later chapters of this book.

1971, Burbidge, G. R., Burbidge, E. M., Solomon, P. M., and Strittmatter, P. A., Astrophys. Journ., 170, p. 233.

This is an investigation of an independent set of quasars falling close to bright galaxies. The analysis shows accidental chances are less than five in a thousand.

1972, Burbidge, G. R., O'Dell, S. L., and Strittmatter, P. A., Astrophys. Journ., 175, p. 601.

This analysis showed quasars associated with more distant galaxies fell closer to the galaxies on the sky as if viewed from a greater distance. This relation was confirmed and expanded by Arp in 1983 (see below). The discussion in the Burbidge, O'Dell, and Strittmatter paper developed all the properties of the quasars' distribution in space which had to pertain if they were more local than their redshift distances. These distribution properties were later confirmed by subsequent evidence discussed in this book.

1973, Arp, H., Confrontation of Cosmological Theories with Observational Data, IAU Symposium No. 63, ed. by M. S. Longair, D. Reidel, Dordrecht, Holland, p. 61.

This is a brief summary of observational evidence for nonvelocity-caused redshifts to that date. It gives the first evidence for absolute luminosities of quasars as a function of their (intrinsic) redshift which will be elaborated in later chapters.

1973, Arp, H., Evidence for Nonvelocity Redshifts—New Evidence and Review, IAU Symposium No. 58, ed. J. R. Shakeshaft, D. Reidel Publishing Co., Dordrecht, Holland, p. 197.

This is a review of work up to 1973 and points again to the quasars near redshift 2 being the less luminous quasars and projected at relatively large separations from very nearby galaxies. This prevision is confirmed and elaborated in the more recent results in Chapter 5 of the present book. Just before this presentation at the IAU in Australia (page 195), W. L. W. Sargent gave a statement of the conventional beliefs in this field. It is interesting to read these two papers to contrast the nature of the evidence used. In those days, many astronomers were actively interested in the discordant evidence and it is extremely interesting to read the recorded debate that took place after each of these papers.

1980. Weedman, D. W., Astrophys. Journ., 237, p. 326.

This is the analysis that purports to demonstrate no association between quasars and galaxies but uses an inhomogeneous sample of too distant galaxies.

1981, Sulentic, J. W., Astrophys. Journ. (Letters), 244, p. L53.

This paper repeats the analysis and shows that the quasars are indeed associated with bright galaxies as they were originally reported to be in the papers commencing in 1966

1982, Webster, A., Mon. Not. Roy. Astron. Soc., 200, p. 47.

The first strong attack against the statistics of the association of quasars with companion galaxies. This is the paper that, though incorrect, was generally accepted as the refutation of the association.

1982, Browne, I. A. W., Astrophys. Journ. (Letters), 263, p. L7.

This and the reply immediately following it in the *Journal* discusses some of the pros and cons of calculating statistics in various ways.

1983, Arp, H., Astrophys. Journ. (Letters), 271, p. L41.

This is the addendum which, with great difficulty, I succeeded in getting published. It discusses the Note Added in Proof to the Browne (1982) paper and points out errors in the Webster (1982) analysis.

1983, Zuiderwijk, E. J. and de Ruiter, H. R., Monthly Notices of the Royal Astronomical Society, 204, p. 675.

This is an independent calculation on the Arp data dealing with quasars near companion galaxies. The authors find evidence that the two kinds of objects are associated. The significance of their association would be much stronger, however, if they took into account the different distances of the galaxies in the sample. For example, the quasar somewhat brighter than 16th mag. about 1/2 degree from NGC 3077 (a companion to M81), is just as much a confirmation of the association as fainter quasars, found at smaller separations from galaxies much more distant.

1983, DuBois, M. A., Giraud, E., and Vigier, J. P., Comptes Rendus Acad. Sci. Paris, 26 Sept. 1983, Serie II-259.
This paper gives a different and elegant statistical confirmation of the associations between quasars and galaxies.

1983, Arp, H., Astrophys. Journ., 271, p. 479.
This is the final paper completing the observations and recalculating probabilities by a different method, and which confirms the original Arp calculation.

1984, Chu, Y., Zhu, X., Burbidge, G., and Hewitt, A., Astronomy and Astrophysics, 138, p. 408.
This is the most recent paper confirming the association of quasars with nearby galaxies.

GALAXIES VISIBLY 3
CONNECTED
TO QUASARS

It seems exceedingly strange to have battled so hard about statistics when direct photographic evidence of physical connections between quasars and low-redshift galaxies has existed all along. We saw one example of this in Figure 1-3. But here I will recount briefly the saga of a much more famous case, the greatly tortured history of the galaxy NGC 4319 and its nearby companion.

The story begins with the astronomer called Markarian who surveyed the sky for objects with strong ultraviolet continuum radiation using a small Schmidt telescope in Armenia. He found among his hotly radiating objects the quasar-like object, called Markarian 205, close to the edge of a spiral galaxy. Daniel Weedman obtained spectra and announced that it had a redshift of $z = 21,000$ km s^{-1}. But the galaxy only had a redshift of $z = 1,700$ km s^{-1}.

Naturally, I was interested whether any effects were visible in the two objects which might give direct evidence that they were close to each other in space. To make sure, I took the deepest photograph possible, using the high-detectivity IIIa-J film that Eastman Kodak had manufactured especially for astronomy. It required a four-hour, sky-limited exposure at the prime focus of the 200-inch reflector at Mt. Palomar. When I developed the photograph I was surprised and excited to find a luminous connection between the quasar and the galaxy. Naturally, the first thing I did was to ask myself whether this could be some kind of artifact, or was it a real luminous connection. An observer experienced with large telescopes (the older variety of observers at least) can look at a photographic plate and ascertain from the sharpness, shape, and extent of an image whether it is likely to be an emulsion defect or a real object in the sky. This object was clearly real. The next question which naturally presented itself was: Since the quasar and galaxy were close on the plate, could this apparent connection be due to overlapping of projected images, that is, a bleeding together of the light distribution around accidentally projected background and foreground objects? A few moments' thought indicated that unrelated images melding together would produce an hourglass-shaped image. But, in fact, the photographed connection was relatively narrow and straight-sided ruling out anything

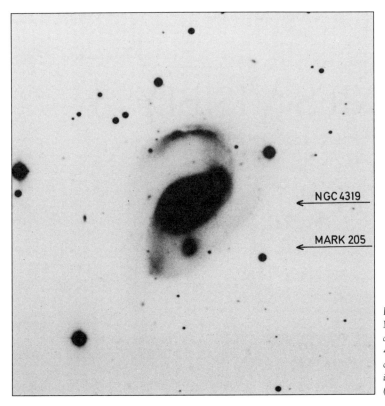

NGC 4319 ←

MARK 205 ←

Figure 3-1. The quasar-like Markarian 205 is just below the disrupted spiral galaxy, NGC 4319. Note the straight, luminous connection between the two. This is the original discovery photograph (Arp 1971).

other than a real physical connection. Figure 3-1 shows this now-famous photograph.

Well didn't it rain! A number of photographs that did not show the connection were soon circulated. It got so bad that at the 1973 meeting in Australia I projected a short exposure of the system, explaining that I did not want people to think I was a bad photographer, and that I too could obtain an exposure that did not show the connection. The feeling that was communicated from little groups of astronomers who would stop talking as I approached was that for the sake of the honor of science they would graciously assume that my original report had been misled by some transient artifact.

The published paper that had the most effect in this little drama was a rather pretentious effort by two researchers at another observatory. With a telescope smaller than the one I had used to obtain my picture, they ob-

tained a new picture. (The ratio of their 2-meter to the 5-meter I had used gives 2/5 squared = 0.16 of the photons.) They proceeded to give the definitive analysis of the system in the following terms: (1) The connection was not there; (2) Just in case it was there, it was accounted for by a background galaxy lying accidentally in just the right position to appear like a connection. In actual fact, the connection had much too low a surface brightness to be a galaxy seen edge-on. The connection was also straight-sided, whereas an edge-on galaxy would have to taper at its ends. But the taper of an edge-on galaxy would have to be opposite the hourglass-shaped cusp of two images optically melding together, which was the third favorite explanation advanced for the feature. In fact, looking back now, their picture showed quite well the straight-sided connection that was to be confirmed so clearly with later techniques.

But an amalgam of these contradictory rationalizations was soon accepted as sufficient justification for retaining the conventional view that objects with such different redshifts could not be physically close together.

In all this technical obfuscation, however, a very common-sense point was overlooked. The galaxy, NGC 4319, is an extremely unusual galaxy. It is literally coming apart, as Figure 3-1 or any of the many pictures in the literature attest. There might be a weak attempt to claim there is another large galaxy some distance away that is interacting with NGC 4319. But there are no sheared plumes or asymmetric gravitational tides present in NGC 4319. It is simply that the arms are coming off at the roots in NGC 4319! It is as if this was a normal, two-armed spiral galaxy that had recently (of the order of ten million years ago—a fraction of a galaxy rotation period) suffered some explosion or internal perturbation that simply caused the spiral arms to disintegrate at their base where they normally join the main body of the galaxy. As a long-time observer of peculiar galaxies, I can assure you that this is an extremely unusual spiral galaxy.

The importance of the luminous connection reaching from the quasar-like object back to the galaxy is that the connection goes straight back towards the galaxy's nucleus. This provides rather direct evidence that the quasar emerged from the nucleus. Since nuclei of many galaxies are active, in the sense that they emit high-energy radiation, show variability, and eject radio sources and luminous material, it is logical to conclude that this quasar has been ejected from the nucleus of NGC 4319. If the conditions in the nucleus of the galaxy from which it has been ejected are abnormal, the material out of which the quasar itself is constructed may very well be intrinsically abnormal. We will develop this theme in coming chapters but it has always seemed to me that their probable ejection is the biggest single clue to the nature of quasars. Of course, this makes the whole question of the reality of the connection absolutely crucial.

The question appears to have been resolved by an analysis performed eleven years later by Jack Sulentic with the powerful image-processing facilities of the Jet Propulsion Laboratory in Pasadena. The large computers that had been used to process the pictures of planets and moons sent by the world's first space voyagers had also been programmed with sophisticated algorithms which could extract the maximum information contained in any medical pictures, high-altitude pictures of the Earth's surface and even astronomical photographs. Jean Lorre— who has unfortunately left the image-processing laboratory now— tutored Sulentic in what are still today the most advanced techniques of image processing. Sulentic selected from photographs which had been collected during the 11-year interval the four best plates taken with the 5-meter telescope at Palomar and the three best plates taken with the 4-meter telescope at Kitt Peak National Observatory (KPNO). From this new and independent plate material obtained with the best telescope he produced the picture shown in Figure 3-2.

Figure 3-2 looks just like the original Arp photograph in Figure 3-1. It seems as though the connection does exist! Furthermore, by using the technique of mathematically filtering the information contained in the photographs, Sulentic was able to show a very narrow, sinuous connection inside the broad connection which can be traced well back through the inner regions toward the nucleus of NGC 4319.

The implication of this is crucial. It implies that the quasar-like object, at least as it traversed the galaxy disk, was very small. This makes good sense, and in fact would almost have to be true, if the object was to emerge from within the small dimensions of the cen-

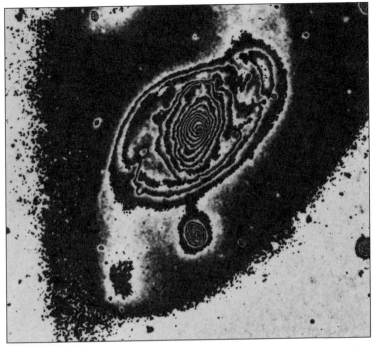

Figure 3-2. This is the confirmation of the connection between NGC 4319 and Mark 205 from the summation of 7 additional plates by Jack Sulentic (1983).

tral nucleus, where the activity of galaxies seems to be centered. At this later date, the luminosity of the quasar may be higher than when it emerged. In any case, it now burns out a large region around its center. It would be extremely interesting to see just how small a center the light in Markarian 205 presently defines. A few seconds of exposure with the Hubble Space telescope would give us this information.

But, the feuding over Markarian 205/ NGC 4319 was far from over. The observers A. Stockton, P. Wehinger, and S. Wyckoff, had been taking and analyzing photographs of the system and claiming that the connection was not real. The latter two authors went so far as to publish pictures in pseudo-color in Sky and Telescope. In a brief article they managed to mention three times in three paragraphs that the quasar must be a background object. They ended with the statement that their Hawaiian observations had established this "beyond a doubt." Their article caused some amusement because their pseudo-color pictures showed the connection between the two objects quite plainly—in fact, if you held the magazine at arm's length the connection virtually leaped off the page!

In view of the massive negative folklore that had preceded Sulentic's image-processed picture of the luminous bridge, we thought that perhaps a little overkill might not hurt. Also, we were interested in finding out more about this object, so we applied for time on the 4-meter KPNO telescope, which had been equipped with the newest highly quantum efficient CCD's (charged coupled devices) for direct imaging. It took the personal intervention of the director, G. R. Burbidge, to get us a couple of nights on this instrument. But with these few hours we were able to obtain images of the object in several different colors. By that time, I had taken temporary refuge at ESO (European Southern Observatory) in Munich. Since they had good computer reduction facilities, I personally did the image processing on these new CCD frames. I used pseudo-color to delineate the bridge in living scarlet as shown on the jacket of this book and in black and white in Figure

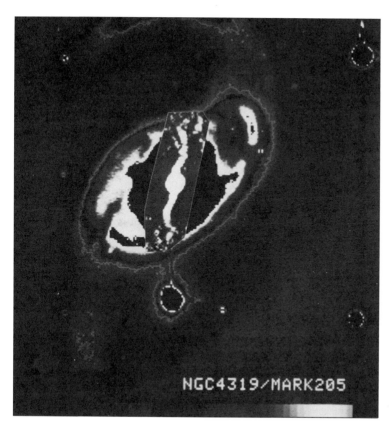

NGC4319/MARK205

Figure 3-3. The picture shows the addition of CCD frames taken at the KPNO 4-meter telescope. The isophotes which best show the bridge between the two objects are colored red in the picture which is on the jacket of this book (Arp and Sulentic, unpublished). The insert shown here in the central region of the galaxy uses image processing to reveal a narrow central spine.

3-3. We joked that perhaps we should make up T-shirts with a superposed outline of the Golden Gate Bridge between the two objects. We abandoned the project, however, when we considered how little sense of humor there was in the field. At any rate, Figure 3-3 is not bad for the bridge that could not be!

The atmospheric steadiness was not good enough on these particular nights to confirm the very thin sinuous connection back to the nucleus. But, the linear intensity response of the sensitive detector allowed image processing of somewhat broader features in the interior by Sulentic which revealed a narrow central spine stretching outward in either direction from the nucleus of the spiral galaxy. This central spine is shown in the inset in Figure 3-3. This latter feature is important for three reasons: First, it demonstrates once again that this is a highly unusual galaxy; sec-

ond, that this unusual feature is associated with the luminous bridge to Markarian 205; and third, that this relatively thin feature suggests a counter-ejection in the opposite direction from the hypothesized ejection of Markarian 205. In astronomy, jets tend to have counter-jets, radio-source ejections tend to occur in opposite directions and, in general, to conserve a momentum in any ejection process one would expect a counter-ejection. It was therefore with considerable excitement that Sulentic spotted a stellar-appearing object in our ultraviolet CCD frames. It was almost exactly at the end of the spine, opposite to Markarian 205. After scrambling to get time on the 4-meter again (the Palomar 5-meter had by this time been completely closed off to us), we tried to get spectra of this faint blue object buried in the disk of the galaxy. We are not sure we got it. There was a little emission on some of our spectra near this position. Perhaps this is an H II region as found normally in spiral galaxies. Perhaps this kind of a hydrogen emission (H II) region, as in some other objects, is an indicator of recent ejection activity. Perhaps this is some gas heated by a continuum source of unknown nature. We need more investigation of this region.

But all of the spectra throughout the disk of NGC 4319 that we did get revealed an unexpected aspect. The hydrogen-alpha emission that normally characterizes spiral galaxies was almost completely absent. Pervading the entire disk was, instead, only emission from ionized nitrogen. This is very unusual for a spiral galaxy and, again, hints that violent events may have recently taken place. This observation also needs to be followed up.

An interesting footnote to the controversy over Markarian 205 and NGC 4319 is that a Caltech astronomer and a regularly collaborating fellow British scientist were in the favored position of regularly obtaining the biggest blocks, really enormous amounts of time, on the 5-meter telescope at Mt. Palomar. One of their favorite observing programs attempts to examine high-redshift objects close to low-redshift objects. If they detect absorption lines of the low-redshift objects in the spectra of the high-redshift objects, they announce them as proof that the high-redshift objects are the more distant. Of course, the high-redshift object could be just behind the low, or even imbedded in it, or, if it was ejected, have pulled out a plume of the low-redshift material around it. Be that as it may, when they don't find the low-redshift absorption, there is an implication that the high-redshift object is in front. (This is not ironclad, of course, because we may be looking through a "chink" in the low-redshift object.) But in the case of NGC 4319 just discussed, the material in the galaxy is so spread around, that it would be difficult to imagine finding a column to look through that was free from low-redshift gas. So I noted

quietly the information that had been leaked to me about a year before that they had looked hard for low-redshift absorption in the spectrum of Markarian 205. From the floor of the Liege meeting in 1983, I asked what they had found. They replied that they had found no absorption. What seemed to me quite devastating was that they had to publicly admit that they had not published information gained from those enormous amounts of large telescope time, that they had withheld this important scientific information apparently because it did not agree with the position to which they were committed.

The most recent development in the saga of this system is quite spectacular. Thanks to the dedicated perserverance of Sulentic, he was able to obtain 6 hours of observing with the Very Large Array radio telescope. His results are shown in Figure 3-4. This, the most sensitive radio map obtained to date, now clearly shows extended lobes of radio emission on either side of the galaxy. Therefore, like other examples of ejecting galaxies, NGC 4319 also turns out to have ejected radio material on either side of its nucleus. It is an enormously rare *spiral* galaxy, however, which shows such ejected radio material beyond its nucleus. (One other, NGC 4258, will be discussed in Chapter 9.) The rare, quasar-like object, Markarian 205, is closer to the nucleus than these extended lobes and its line to the nucleus is rotated slightly forward, in the direction of rotation of the galaxy, as if it were a slightly later ejection. The galaxy's explosive disruption is also confirmed by the observation of the ejected radio lobes.

The grand, final question now becomes: "Does all this evidence finally add up to conclusive proof of what was immediately evident from studying the first photograph: namely, that these two cosmic objects of extremely different redshifts are physically related, that in fact the higher redshift, compact object has been ejected from the lower redshift galaxy?"

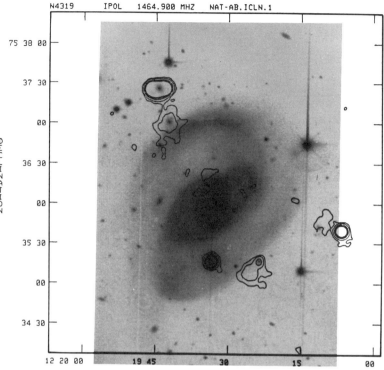

N4319   IPOL   1464.900 MHZ   NAT-AB.ICLN.1

Figure 3-4. Radio emission from NGC 4319 as measured by Sulentic with the Very Large Array radio telescope (at 20-cm wavelength). The radio isophotes are superimposed on a photograph taken in red light with a CCD detector. Radio lobes are seen on either side of the nucleus of the galaxy, and the quasar, like examples which follow in this chapter, is very near one of the radio lobes.

B. The Quasar PKS 1327-206: Another Quasar Connected to a Peculiar Galaxy

If the preceding examples which have been discussed were not sufficient, the most conclusive example of a quasar connected to a galaxy turned up during the writing of this book. The way in which it surfaced is perhaps as revealing as the fact of the association. As just mentioned, one of the most popular types of time allotments on telescopes involves long exposures on the spectra of quasars near galaxies. The game is to search for absorption lines in the quasar due to the "foreground" galaxy and thus to study the halo surrounding the foreground galaxy. (This postulated halo is not optically visible.) As usual, no result is too "gee whiz" not to be easily fitted into a model of halos. (Of course, it is strongly preferred that examples of quasars close to galaxies are discovered by observers of cosmological rather than local persuasion.)

In this particular case, I was in Paris giving a series of lectures on the latest evidence for association of quasars with nearby galaxies. Announcements of these lectures had been widely posted, but during the course of these weeks, I took the occasion to call on some close astronomical friends who did not know I was there. Naturally, they began to entertain me with their latest results on galaxy halos by using quasars as test probes in the background. I was listening politely to tales of a particular unusual halo when I casually asked, "What does the adjacent galaxy look like?"

There was a considerable silence after which it developed that they, neither separately nor together, had ever looked at pictures of the pair of objects they were studying—at least not at the best pictures, which were available to everyone in the form of the Schmidt telescope IIIa-J sky survey. I immediately proceeded to consult the nearest cataloged photographs. It turned out that two

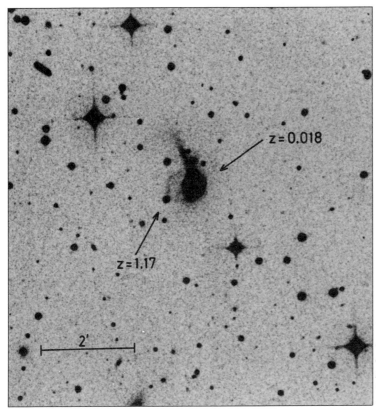

z=0.018

z=1.17

2'

Figure 3-5. The quasar, Parkes 1327-206 connected by a luminous filament to a galaxy with a jet. Print is from two survey plates taken with U.K. Schmidt telescope in Australia. Copyright Royal Observatory, Edinburgh.

independent photographs of this system existed and both plainly showed a luminous filament connecting the quasar to the galaxy. Figure 3-5 shows the combined print of these two survey photographs.

The analysis of this photograph seems very simple to me. There are only two possibilities. Either the quasar placed at the head of the filament is an accident, or the two objects are physically connected. Since the configuration has negligible probability of arising by chance, I conclude that this demonstrates the physical association of quasar and galaxy. There goes the whole cosmological quasar hypothesis!

I might remark that one interpretation of what is going on in this picture might be that the quasar originated at a point that is now in the strong jet which emerges from the galaxy, and that both quasar and galaxy have moved away slightly from that point since that time of origin. Another interpretation, since the quasar is quite bright in apparent magnitude, is that, along the lines of Chapter 5, they could both be close to us in space and have been expelled by a nearby galaxy. They might also simply represent a rare accidental collision of a galaxy and quasar in the same locality of space. One thing that is inescapable, however, is that the high redshift quasar is at the same distance as the low redshift galaxy.

Another aspect that is inescapable, unfortunately, is that there was a considerable amount of throat-clearing and sidelong glances but that picture was not rushed into the scientific literature. In fact, it was not published at all. I am conducting a two-part scientific experiment with this object. The proposition is that when conclusive evidence for the association of high and low redshift objects exists, it goes unnoticed. When it is pointed out, it is not published. The first part of the proposition has already been verified. The second part of the proposition is being tested. I made photographs of the objects available in June 1984. My prediction is that the pictures will be seen only upon the publication of the present book.

There has been another interesting mechanism at work over the years which I am only now beginning to appreciate to its fullest. It goes something this this:

"This is a very impressive picture of a high-redshift object connected to a low-redshift object. If you can show me another one of these, I will have to take the matter seriously."

When the next, but even more striking object is discovered:

"Oh now, this is really impressive. Forget the first one. It requires another one of these."

C. NGC 5297/96 and Other Galaxies Optically Connected to or Perturbed by Quasars

Featured on the cover of the published proceedings of the Paris Conference of 1976 was a large spiral galaxy, NGC 5297, with a conspicuous companion galaxy, NGC 5296. It is shown here in Figure 3-6. A diffuse, luminous connection extends from the companion in toward the main galaxy and a similar extension in the other direction terminates on a quasar.

The story of this quasar's discovery may seem unbelievable to skeptics, but I do have a witness. Jack Sulentic and I were going through the Palomar Sky Survey prints making identification prints for our next telescope run. I spotted this galaxy with its companion and said, "That's the kind of companion that should have a quasar." We looked at the nearest star to the companion and it was blue. We

took a spectrum that run and it turned out to be a quasar. (This occurred before the systematic search for quasars around companions which was subsequently performed in another area of the sky, as described in Chapter 2.) The chance of accidentally finding a quasar both this bright and this close to NGC 5296 is only about 0.002 or 2 chances in a thousand. After the quasar was confirmed, the deep photograph shown in Figure 3-6 was obtained with the 200-inch telescope. It was then discovered that there was a low surface brightness filament leading from NGC 5296, narrowing as it approaches the quasar and ending almost exactly on the quasar.

On this same deep plate a small compact galaxy was seen silhouetted against the companion galaxy, NGC 5296, which meant that it had to be spatially in front of the companion. Yet, the compact galaxy's redshift is more than $\triangle z = 23,000$ km s^{-1} greater. This is the first example we have encountered of a galaxy, an object with larger apparent diameter than the generally point source quasars, which has an "excess" or nonvelocity redshift. In Chapter 6 we will see many examples of galaxies with excess redshifts and propose a way in which the anomalous redshifts of these galaxies are related to those of quasars.

At the Paris Conference, further cases were reported of a companion galaxy with a luminous filament pointing toward a nearby quasar (NGC 5682, shown here in Fig. 2-3, also accompanied by a nearby, high-redshift Markarian Object). Reported in addition was a quasar within the envelope of a peculiar E-galaxy, apparently perturbing it (NGC 7413). Another high-redshift, very peculiar object was found silhouetted in front of the outskirts of the nearby E-galaxy (NGC 1199).

In the decade since these discoveries were announced there has been no serious follow-up observations by other astronomers. In fact, there has been a clear effort to avoid these objects.

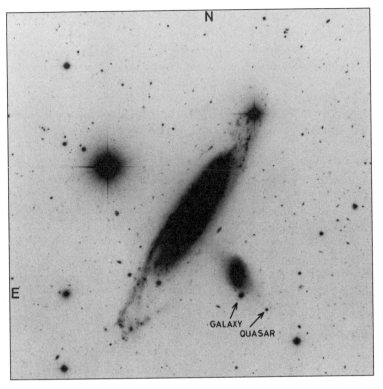

GALAXY

QUASAR

Figure 3-6. The spiral galaxy NGC 5297, and its companion galaxy NGC 5296. Arrows indicate quasar of redshift z = 0.96 and silhouetted high-redshift galaxy of redshift z = 25,900 km s^{-1}.

D. Radio Connections—The Radio Galaxy 3C 303 and Nearby Quasar(s)

Not all radiating filaments emerging from galaxies are seen in visible-light wavelengths. In fact, it is much more common to see jets of radio-emitting material emerging from galaxies. It is believed that inside these radio jets are ionized gases (plasmas) where the motions of the charged particles are bent by magnetic lines of force causing radiation. (Accelerating or decelerating electrons produce so-called synchrotron radiation which, for the lower energies, is generally detected as radio emission.) What causes these jets is more or less a mystery, although most theorists talk about a "beam" of energetic particles being ejected somehow from active galactic nuclei. Now, I personally have severe doubts whether beams can explain the observed morphologies—the jets are in many cases too thin and parallel-sided and the "hot spots" (compact regions of intense radio emission) observed in the outer

lobes tend to trail behind the jets. But if compact bodies can be ejected from nuclei, as the evidence just described implies, perhaps a more or less continuous stream of particles can accompany them. Alternatively if a beam of smaller particles becomes narrow enough and in addition must turn off and on, i.e., be pulsed, perhaps it approaches, in some sense, our crude concept of whatever a compact quasar-like or proto-quasar-like object might be during its ejection from a galaxy. Perhaps it does not pay to be too dogmatic at this stage about just exactly what is ejected from these nuclei.

Regardless of the exact composition of the jet, however, if we observe a quasar out near the end of a radio jet where it has low probability of appearing by accident, it becomes an additional demonstration of the association of quasars with lower redshift galaxies. The quasars then are connected to the galaxies not by an optically radiating fila-

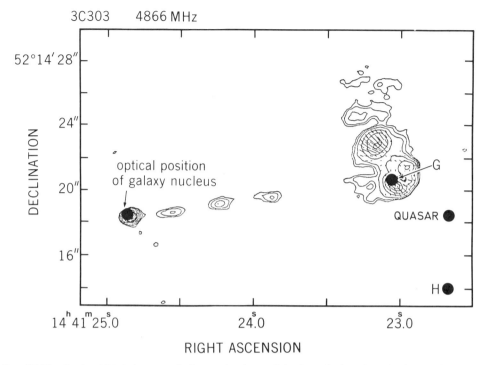

Figure 3-7. *The radio galaxy 3C 303, showing ejected radio material to the west which ends near the objects discussed in the text. Radio map from P. Kronberg, E. M. Burbidge, H. E. Smith, and R. G. Strom.*

ment as before, but by a radio radiating filament. Several examples of this exist and one of the best known is shown in Figure 3-7. In that figure, we see the radio filament extending westward to where it terminates at the position of three, stellar-appearing, ultraviolet objects. One of these objects has been confirmed to be a quasar by E.M. Burbidge, P. Kronberg, H. E. Smith and R. Strom. The other two are somewhat too faint to get a decisive spectrum on. But the expectation would have to be that they also are some kind of quasars or quasar-like objects. The probability of getting three such objects so close together is extremely small, marking this configuration as a very unusual one. But, just considering the one confirmed quasar, we see that it falls only 5 arcsec from the tip of the radio jet. By the precepts of Chapter 1 the likelihood of this occurring by chance is something like $\leq 10^{-4}$. Thus this example

provides additional, very strong evidence for the connection of a relatively low-redshift galaxy with a quasar.

E. The Radio Galaxy 0844 + 31

Curiously enough another radio galaxy looks quite similar to the one we have just discussed. This latter galaxy is called 0844+31 (after its position in the sky), or 4C 31.32 (after its position in the 4th Cambridge Catalog of radio sources). The radio map of this object is shown in Figure 3-8.

A strong radio jet proceeds roughly northward from the galaxy. It ends in a lobe of radio emission within which there is a "hot spot." This hot spot curves around in a southerly direction and ends about 5 arcsec from a quasar. Again, by using the average quasar density discussed in Chapter 1, we can calculate the chance of a quasar this bright acci-

0844+31

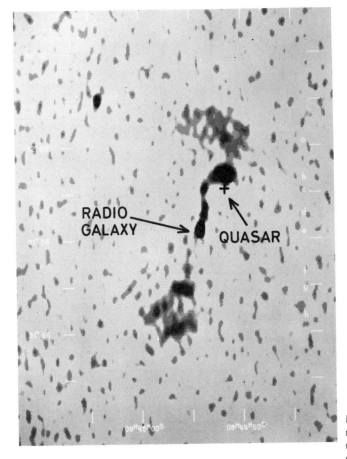

DEC.

RADIO GALAXY

QUASAR

R.A.

Figure 3-8. The radio isophotes of the galaxy 0844+31 measured at 6-cm wavelength. The cross shows the position of a quasar with $z = 1.83$. Observations by W. van Breugel.

dentally falling this close to the tip of the hot spot: it is 3×10^{-6}. That is less than one chance in 330,000. Even if we say the significant distance is from the quasar to the center of the radio lobe, about 19 arcsec, the chances of accidental occurrence are only 4×10^{-5}, or about one chance in 25,000.

But how many chances did we have to accidentally discover these quasar juxtapositions with radio jets? In the most recent compilation, A. Bridle and R. Perley list only 75 galaxies with redshift $z \lesssim 0.2$ that have radio

jets. For the astronomers who studied these objects, just unavoidable encounters with known quasars have turned up the two associations in this list (0844+31 and 3C 303) both at an improbability level of less than 10^{-4}. What would a quasar search around the rest of these radio jets reveal? My casual inspection of the list indicates there may be as many as eleven associations, at about the 0.01 level of improbability, of radio-jet galaxies with already known active objects of higher redshift in the vicinity, some with good alignment with the radio jets.

These associations "get no respect" because in each individual case the high-redshift object is dismissed as an unrelated background object. Then, each case is forgotten. One of the purposes of this book is to collect together these neglected cases in order to show that they are not isolated incidents but together furnish another powerful confirmation of the ejection origin of quasars and quasar-like objects from active, low-redshift galaxies.

Actually, when unusual objects like quasars fall this close to the end of a radio or optical jet, the question should *not* be: Can we measure a slight separation between the two which we can use as an excuse to ignore the observation? After all, as discussed in this book, a lot of independent evidence strongly established these kinds of associations. The question should be, what does the slight separation mean? Are quasars and compact objects slightly preceding, or trailing, the connection? Are they exhibiting the same kind of behavior as the ejected emission regions in the galaxy NGC 1808, where G. Schnurr reports a line of blue luminous regions slightly separated from the hydrogen-alpha emitting regions? Is the optical object a leading precursor or a later development in the ejection? Can compact objects power the radio lobes, and are they the source of *in situ* energy injection?

F. A Quasar and Compact Radio Sources Ejected from The Radio Galaxy B2 0924 + 30

During the course of a survey of radio sources with the radio telescope in Bologna, Italy, a very interesting radio galaxy was discovered. Like so many radio galaxies, this one had lobes of radio emission stretching away on either side of it. The lobes are material ejected from the nucleus of the galaxy, according to the accepted belief. But, in this particular case, three very compact radio sources are almost perfectly aligned with this ejection. The authors of this paper, R. Ekers, R. Fanti, C. Lari, and M.-H. Ulrich, calculated the chance of these compact sources being so situated was only about 10^{-5}, or one in a hundred thousand. Yet the nearest compact source was almost touching one of the large outer lobes of the radio galaxy!

Figure 3-9 shows this configuration.

Since I was observing on the 200-inch telescope in those days, I was able to measure the extremely faint optical object at the position of the nearest compact radio source. It was a quasar of redshift $z = 2.02$!

There are several comments we can make about this:

With the powerful radio telescopes now available (at considerable public expense) this region could be mapped to much fainter contour levels. It is quite possible the slight space between the quasar and the extended radio lobe would then turn out to be filled in by radio emission, furnishing a continuous connection between the ejected material of the galaxy and the quasar. In any event, a deeper radio map could give critical information on the kind of connectivity or interaction that this quasar had with the lobe, if indeed it does interact.

The second comment is that this system could be critical for understanding the way in which galaxies eject quasars. Since the quasar which was observed was so optically faint, the system could be fairly distant and there could additionally be even fainter quasars, which we cannot yet see, at the positions of the two other impact sources. If the outer two compact sources are quasars, why are they fainter? Are they closer to their birth? If so, measuring their redshifts would be critical because it might confirm the suggestion that quasars are born with very high redshifts and evolve toward brighter, lower-redshift objects with time. In other words, quasars might represent

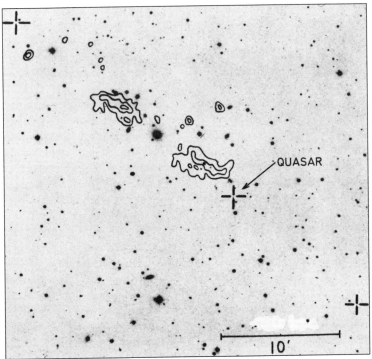

Figure 3-9. The radio galaxy B2 0924+30, showing ejected radio lobes and aligned compact radio sources. The nearest compact source to the southwest radio lobe is a quasar of $z = 2.02$. Radio contours from Ekers, Fanti, Lari, and Ulrich.

the birth of galaxies as in conventional theories, but they simply start small and grow larger. Furthermore, there may be many such emerging sources located throughout much of relatively nearby space.

Of course, there are many other possibilities. One is that the outer compact sources were ejected at greater speed or that they were ejected at an earlier time. The outer sources might also be different kinds of objects, or the speed of ejection may have had some effect on the rate of their development, so that they are now still below our limit of detection. Large telescopes exploring the region of the outer compact radio sources like these could reveal important new information which would aid in understanding just how fast quasars are ejected and how rapidly they evolve. But who will use large telescopes for those investigations?

We can summarize the content of this chapter by saying there are a number of exam-

ples already known of an *"experimentum crucis"* where a quasar is seen linked directly to a low-redshift galaxy. Any one of these is sufficient to establish conclusively that quasars can be much closer than their redshift distances. But a number of these conclusive cases now exist. And, of course, this is all in addition to the statistics of multiple and single associations developed in the first two chapters, which I also feel are conclusive.

The very close separation of one to three quasars from a galaxy or the visible connection to a specific galaxy, however, are far from the most common form of associations. In the coming chapters we will see that the most common form of quasar associations is in groups and lines at many diameters from their galaxies of origin. These associations are generally supported by the morphology of the central galaxy, the distribution of radio material and the distribution of X-ray material in the vicinity.

TABLE 3-1
Quasars Connected to Galaxies or Close to Radio Lobes

GALAXY		QUASAR				
Name	Redshift km/s	Name	Dist. (arcsec)	Mag.	Redshift (z)	Chance Probability
NGC 4319	1,700	Mark 205	40	14.5	0.07	~ 0
MCG 03-34-085	5,400	PKS 1327-206	38	17.0	1.17	~ 0
NGC 5296	2,500	BSO#1	55	19.3	0.96	$\ll 10^{-3}$
3C 303	42,000	UV#C	20*	20	1.57	$\lesssim 10^{-4}$
IC 2402	20,000	0844+31	70*	18.0	1.83	$\sim 10^{-5}$
0924+30	8,000	Compact Source	497*	21.5	2.02	$\sim 10^{-5}$

*Distance from galaxy; quasar is much closer to hot spot or radio lobe.

Appendix to Chapter 3

1971, Arp, H., Astrophys. Letters, 9, p. 1.
The original picture of the connection between Markarian 205 and NGC 4319 was published here (Fig. 3-1 in the present book). The object was also discussed in the "Redshift Controversy" (loc. cit. Chap. 1) and in following references:

1972, Lynds, R. and Millikan, A. G., Astrophys. Journ. (Letters), 176, p. L5.

1979, Stockton, A., Wyckoff. S., and Wehinger, P., Astrophys. Journ., 231, p. 673.

1981, Wyckoff, S. and Wehinger, P. A., Sky and Telescope, 61, p. 200 (March 1981).
The connection is conspicuous in pseudo-color in this last publication, even while the authors state that they have established beyond any doubt that Markarian 205 is ten times more distant!

1983, Sulentic, J. W., Astrophys. Journ. (Letters), 265, p. L49.
This is the image processing work that confirmed the broad connection (Fig. 3-2) and discovered the sinuous connection back to NGC 4319 discussed in this chapter.

1984, Kunth, D. and Bergeron J., Mon. Not. Roy. Astron. Soc., 210, p. 873.
The subject of this paper is the strong sodium absorption in the spectrum of the quasar, PKS 1327-206 due to the adjacent peculiar galaxy. When examined on cataloged photographs, the system appears connected as shown in Figure 3-5.

1976 "Paris Conference" IAU Colloque No. 37—Decalages vers le rouge et l' expansion de l'univers,—eds. C. Balkowski and B. E. Westerlund (Paris Centre National de la Recherche Scientifique Colloques Internationaux No. 263), p. 377 and other articles.
Because part of the subject of this conference was anomalous redshift, the International Astronomical Union (IAU) did not want it to be at the elevated status of a symposium. Only with pressure from some French astronomers was it able to go forward and then as a colloquium only. Nevertheless, the conference produced the best summary of anomalous redshift data to that date, by a number of contributors, and should have established beyond doubt the existence of these effects.

1977, Kronberg, P., Burbidge, E. M., Smith, H. E., and Strom, R. G., Astrophys. Journ. 218, p. 8.

This paper discusses the relation of the quasar and the ultraviolet objects to the radio galaxy 3C 303.

1974, Grueff, G. and Vigotti, M., Astron. and Astrophys., 35, p. 491.

1977, van Breugel, W.J.M. and Miley, G.K., Nature, 265, p. 315.

1980, van Breugel, W.J.M., Astron. and Astrophys., 81, p. 275.

All these papers discuss the radio jet galaxy, 0844 + 31.

1975, Ekers, R., Fanti, R., Lari, C., and Ulrich, M.-H., Nature, 258, p. 584.

This paper reports the alignment of compact radio sources and lobes across the galaxy in the radio source B2 0924 + 30.

CERTAIN 4
GALAXIES WITH
MANY QUASARS

If a few quasars belong to some nearby galaxies, where do the majority of quasars belong? Over three thousand quasars are known now; most of them are spread over large areas of the sky where it is not immediately apparent that they are associated with any particular galaxy. One obvious answer might be, for example, that most quasars were ejected away from their galaxies of origin to mingle somewhere in intergalactic space. Perhaps only a few have been ejected so weakly that they orbit around their galaxy of origin. Perhaps only a few are seen close to the moment of their emergence, where they still show an umbilical attachment to their parent galaxy. But it is possible that sometimes a galaxy might eject many quasars and might be caught in the act of doing this. Could it have been predicted that some galaxies had many associated quasars? If so, it also might have been predicted that they would be encountered unexpectedly.

A. The Galaxy with the Longest Known Optical Jets, NGC 1097

In 1974, I was sitting at a viewing machine in Edinburgh, systematically scanning deep plates of the southern sky taken with the Schmidt telescope in Australia. This was part of a more than ten-year project with Barry Madore that culminated with the publication in 1987 of a two-volume *Catalog of Southern Peculiar Galaxies and Associations*. Someone from the Schmidt Telescope Unit brought me a deep plate of another region.

"Do you see this faint marking pointing at this galaxy?" he asked.

"Well, yes, I see it, but it does not look like features which I've had previous experience with, so I would guess it was not real."

I had made the typical response of the expert and was soon proved to be totally wrong. The discoverers of the jet, R. D. Wolstencroft and W. Zealy, obtained additional independent photographs and proved it was a luminous jet emerging from the galaxy. Their discovery turned out to be the most spectacular example of optical jets found to date.

No one yet has the slightest idea what mysterious process may have caused them.

About one year later, I had a dark-of-the-moon run of about 14 nights in the prime focus cage of the new 4-meter reflector on Cerro Tololo in Chile. The telescope was not

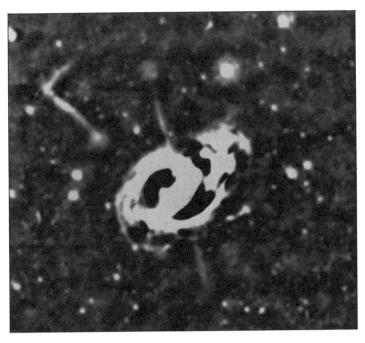

Figure 4-1. The spiral galaxy NGC 1097 and its four optical jets. Photographs by Halton Arp, image-processed by Jean Lorre.

yet commissioned but the director, Victor Blanco, had invited me to test it photographically on objects of particular interest. In this exceptional observing opportunity, one of the objects which had my top priority was the jet galaxy, NGC 1097. From the many limiting photographs that I obtained of the object, Jean Lorre performed a masterful image-processing job. He information-added all the plates, stretched the contrast at the low surface brightness of the jets, and removed all but the largest stars by replacing them with adjacent sky averages. The final, best picture obtained of the jets coming from NGC 1097 is shown in Figure 4-1.

The image processing has brought out the fact that the narrowest jet, proceeding slightly east of north in Figure 4-1 ends in a "puff" of faintly luminous material. Directly opposite, emerging from the opposite side of the galaxy, is a fainter, redder jet, which is clearly the counter-jet to the first. An extremely long, straight jet extends very faintly down to the southwest from the body of the galaxy. It is not quite exactly opposite the fa-

mous "dog-leg" jet which points off toward the northeast. The sudden right-angle turn made at the end of the dog-leg jet has always defied explanation. If it is a secondary ejection, there is no apparent reason why it should make so closely a right-angle bend. Surprisingly, the jets have never been clearly detected in radio emission, not even with the Very Large Array (VLA) radio telescope. There are some slightly higher surface brightness spots in the dog-leg jet which I have measured spectroscopically, but only a very faint, featureless continuum registers, telling us very little about the nature of the condensations.

Detailed photography of the interior of the galaxy reveals a beautiful, two-armed barred spiral. The nuclear region contains unusually large, bright clumps of emission. The galaxy is one of a small group called "hot spot" nucleus galaxies. As accurately as can be determined, the jets emerge directly from the small central nucleus. Figure 4-2 shows the narrow spiral arms delicately outlined by gaseous emission (H II regions). That photo-

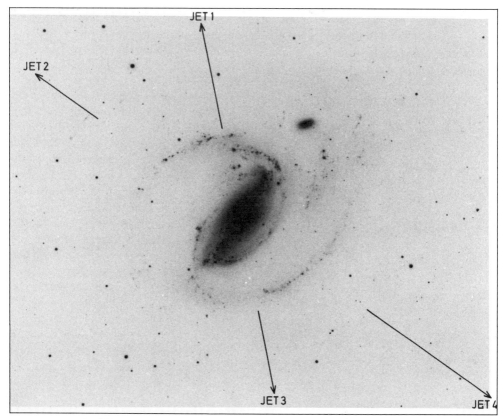

Figure 4-2. Photograph in light of hydrogen emission (Hα) showing spiral arms in the interior of NGC 1097, and rupture of the arm as jet #1 passes through the north arm. Photographs used in this and preceding figure were taken with the CTIO 4-meter telescope (National Optical Astronomy Observatories, operated by the Association of Universities for Research in Astronomy, Inc., under contract with the National Science Foundation).

graph also shows the exciting result that the spiral arm is clearly disrupted just ahead of where the narrowest jet passes out to the north-northeast: We can actually see the physical effects of this jet punching through the spiral arm!

Moreover, because we know the approximate rotation velocity of NGC 1097, we can compute, from the distance that the punctured point on the arm has moved forward, how long ago the event happened. The rotating spiral galaxy is like a great clock in the sky, and although we do not know what has been shot out of the center, we can gather a very good estimate   how long ago it happened. The answer comes out that the event is only about 10^7 years old. Ten million years

is a short time on the scale of the Universe. It is only about one-thirtieth of the time needed for one rotation of a spiral galaxy. I believe these kinds of estimates are the only reliable estimate of the age of whatever it is that has been ejected out of the nucleus of the galaxy. We will see this estimated age of a few times 10^7 years reappearing in other systems to follow. This will become an important datum when we later try to deduce the nature of the ejected material.

It is also interesting to note that with the jets already so faint at such an early age, the implication is that such phenomena are very transitory, so that we should not see many galaxies in such a stage. Moreover, we apparently see these ejecta because the expulsion has gone off in the plane of the galaxy. If many galaxies ejected nonluminous material out of their planes, there could be enormous numbers of similar ejections of which we are completely unaware. Does expulsion in the plane slow the ejecta down so that they remain closer to their galaxy of origin? In Figure 4-2, we see an anomalously large H II region just at the rupture point of the northern arm. Could this somehow be connected with the ejection event? If the ultraviolet object in NGC 4319, which is opposite to Markarian 205 (see Chapter 3), is gaseous emission, could it be related to a similar ejection in the plane? It is amazing that no astronomers are following up these important clues.

The next lurch forward in the study of NGC 1097 was again fortuitous. The object was observed in X-ray wavelengths by the Einstein satellite in January 1979. Eventually it was noticed that there was a lot of X-ray emission on the north side of NGC 1097. Wolstencroft pointed out to me that one X-ray source coincides with a star brighter than 18th magnitude. I opined that this was too bright to be a quasar, but when I took the spectrum, I was wrong again. It was a quasar of redshift $z = 1.00$. Wolstencroft obtained objective-prism plates of the area and we looked around for emission objects. We found six quasars, all in a small area near the northern jets. This corresponded to an over-density from the expected background by a factor of 25. Note that here again we find an over-density of almost exactly the amount found around the galaxies discussed in Chapter 2. The only encouragement we received that this was a significant result was when we encountered great difficulty in getting it published.

It was clear that the situation required another heroic effort to achieve resolution. With a program that was to take three collaborators more than three years we set out to answer the questions: (1) Is the enhanced quasar density present only in the area near the northern jets, or is it more generally present over the area around NGC 1097? (2) With a complete search of a large field around NGC 1097, would the edges of the field approach the background density of quasars found in other parts of the sky?

Good-seeing objective-prism plates were obtained from the Schmidt telescope in Australia. The Chinese astronomer X. T. He searched—and researched—these plates, eventually producing a list of 43 candidates within the central 8.1 square degrees. I measured 33 of these candidates spectroscopically with Carnegie Institution's telescope in Chile. They turned out to be 94% true quasars, the best percentage average for picking quasars I have ever seen. We assume that essentially the whole of the candidate list are quasars and plot their distribution in Figure 4-3.

Figure 4-3 tells the story at a glance. The concentration of quasars toward NGC 1097 is obvious. In addition, the quasar density at the edges of the field drops to just the value expected for an average sky. In order to make the quasar concentration go away, one would have had to miss about 60 quasars in the field, an obviously impossible number. But, of course, finding more quasars in this field would then raise the already significant excess-density of quasars to even larger values.

This result clearly puts the ball in the establishment's court. The return strokes, however, have been less than brilliant. When I showed these results at the Liege Symposium in 1983, everyman's friendly radio astronomer approached me with his usual exquisite blend of pomposity and ineptitude and said, "That's obviously a statistical fluctuation."

After three years of hard work and big telescope time, an anonymous referee reported that the paper "was not in a suitable form for publication." The editor was prepared to allow the referee an open-ended era in which to pursue this opinion but my collaborator, Wolstencroft, produced six pages of closely written statistical computations with

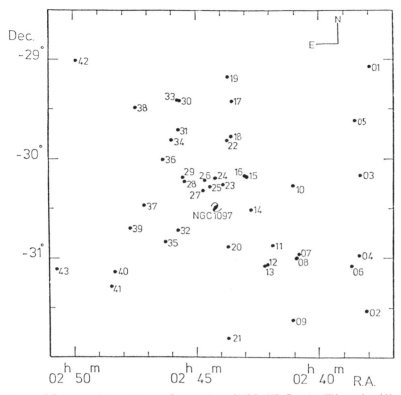

Figure 4-3. Plot of all quasar candidates (94% prove to be quasars) around NGC 1097. From Arp, Wolstencroft, and He.

the result that the paper was eventually published after a delay of only one year and three months.

Certain significant aspects of the NGC 1097 situation, however, serve to introduce the next result in this chapter: (1) The radio emission in NGC 1097 occurs asymmetrically placed over on the side of the strong northern jets. (2) The X-ray emission is asymmetrical, likewise on the side of the northern jets (both the inner and outer X-ray emission). (3) The quasars are preferentially aligned with the jets, more of them being on the side of the northern jets. These latter points are illustrated in Figures 4-4, 4-5, and 4-6.

These are extraordinarily important points because they make clear that the radio and inner X-ray material is associated with the galaxy. Since the quasars are associated with the outer X-ray material, which is con-

tinuous with the inner, and since the quasars are also aligned with the jets, this shows that the association of the quasars cannot be coincidental. It must have some physical significance. Specifically, these results imply that the X-ray material, radio material, and quasars are all part of the ejection which is marked by the optical jets.

Do other examples exist to support this picture?

B. The Disturbed Galaxy NGC 520

The first chapter of this book describes how, in looking around galaxies in the *Atlas of Peculiar Galaxies*, I found apparently associated radio sources and quasars. In order to amplify this point a little here, I should say that these associations were mostly with numbers 100 to 160 in the *Atlas*. Those categories

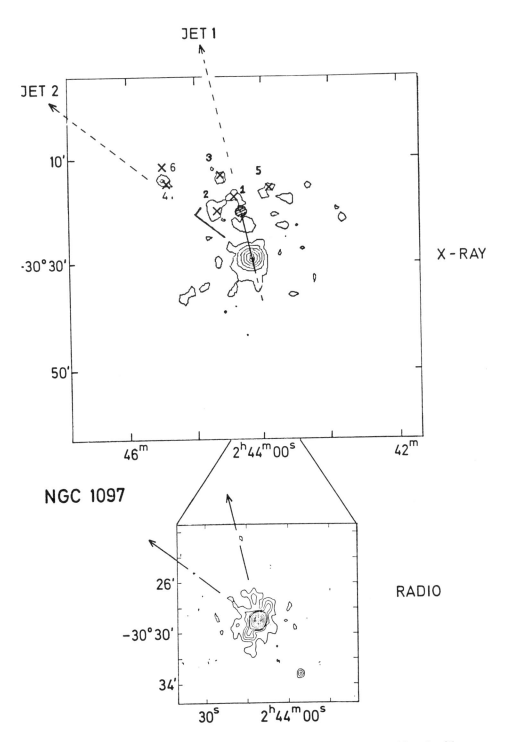

Figure 4-4. X-ray and radio maps of NGC 1097. Note quasars 1 through 6 (X symbols) coincide with many of the patches of X-ray emission. Placement of jets and their extensions indicated by full and dashed lines.

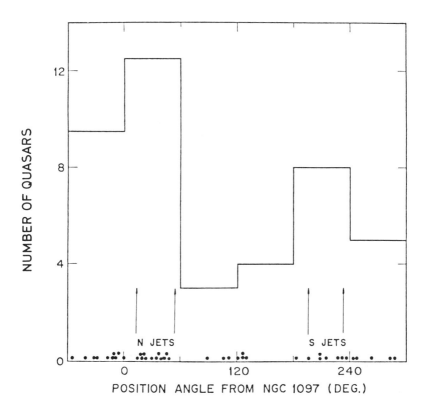

Figure 4-5. The alignment of the direction of all the quasars (filled points) with the direction of the jets in NGC 1097. From Arp, Wolstencroft, and He.

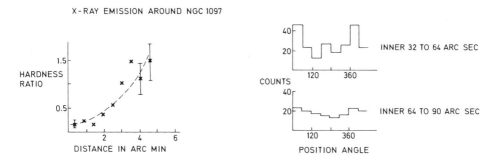

Figure 4-6. These plots demonstrate continuity of high energy to low energy ratio in X-ray sources outward from center of NGC 1097. Also peaks of inner X-rays in direction of strongest jet (pos. angle ≈ 360°). Calculations from Wolstencroft.

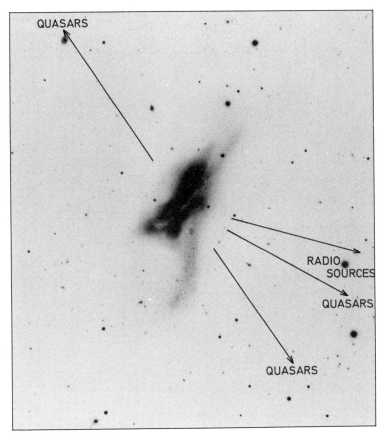

QUASARS

RADIO SOURCES

QUASARS

QUASARS

Figure 4-7. The disturbed galaxy NGC 520. It is number 157 in the Atlas of Peculiar Galaxies. Directions of cone of radio sources discovered in 1967 and lines of quasars discovered in 1970 and 1983 are marked.

in the *Atlas* represent the most chaotic and disturbed objects, presumably contorted by inner activity and explosions. Galaxies in categories with much higher and lower numbers represented a selection of interacting doubles, dwarfs, and other peculiar objects which one would not expect to show violent activity. Thus a significant point, which most critics insisted on overlooking, was that the associations of sources turned out to be primarily with these central numbers in the *Atlas*.

One of the most disturbed objects in the entire Atlas is number 157. It is shown here in Figure 4-7. In 1967, I knew of no quasars around it. I did, however, notice an unusual number of radio sources which appeared to define directions of ejection to the northeast and southwest. Three years later, in 1970, I became aware of four radio-loud quasars to

the southwest. They defined an almost perfect straight line pointing back toward NGC 520. The properties of the quasars in this line resemble each other in a number of ways such that the overall probability of such a chance configuration is less than one in a million. The line of quasars also lies within the previously defined direction of radio source ejection. The line is shown in Figure 4-8.

I remember showing this line of quasars to John Bolton in 1970. As one of the founders of radio astronomy, John has made many identifications of radio sources with quasars over the sky. He said he had not seen any so straight but had seen many approximate lines and apparent chains. It seems amazing that until very recently no one has systematically investigated these features. I suppose the reason is that the configurations involve quasars

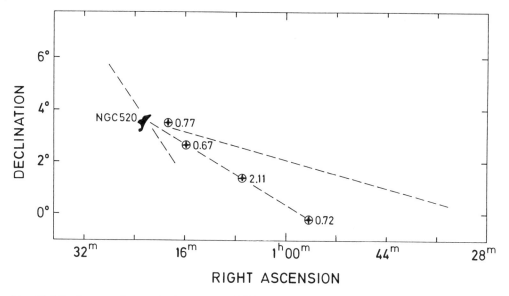

Figure 4-8. *A plot of strongest radio quasars in a larger area around NGC 520. Redshifts are written next to symbols.*

of different redshift.

(Recently, tentative alignment results for faint quasars were put forward in the literature with great difficulty by Clube and Trew, Liege Conference, p. 374 and *Monthly Notices of the Royal Astronomical Society*, submitted.)

Again the investigation of NGC 520 languished, this time for about 10 years, until 1980. By that time, I had started finding quasars over homogeneously searched areas of the sky by using the ultraviolet-excess techniques described in Chapter 2. Jean-Pierre Swings and Jean Surdej of the Institut d'Astrophysique in Liege, Belgium, joined me in a collaborative project of searching several areas of about 20 square degrees each on the sky. I had already obtained plates covering the NGC 520 region but here was an opportunity to have the quasar candidates surveyed by astronomers without previous experience with the region, who would therefore be unbiased.

Over the next few years I measured their candidates with the Carnegie telescope in Chile. The most conspicuous feature in the whole field turned out to be a line of quasars going through NGC 520! In order to make

absolutely sure of this result, I then asked Oscar Duhalde of the Las Campanas Observatory to take an ultraviolet/blue plate on a completely different telescope and the two of us examined independently the 2.1-square-degree field which had been studied around NGC 520. The original search went to 20th apparent magnitude, but to be on the safe side for completeness, we restricted ourselves to quasars brighter than 19th magnitude. Seven quasars resulted from the Swings/Surdej candidates, five on the line and two off. Six additional quasars were found by Arp/Duhalde, one on the line and five off. Swings and Surdej originally were enthusiastic about the line, but after the Liege Conference in 1983, they renounced it, claiming that the association had been found from the Arp/Duhalde search!! The quasars found in this double-independent search of the area around NGC 520 are shown in Figure 4-9 where the reader will have to judge for himself the significance of the line.

It is important to realize that just the distributed quasar density near NGC 520 is, by itself, much higher than in the expected

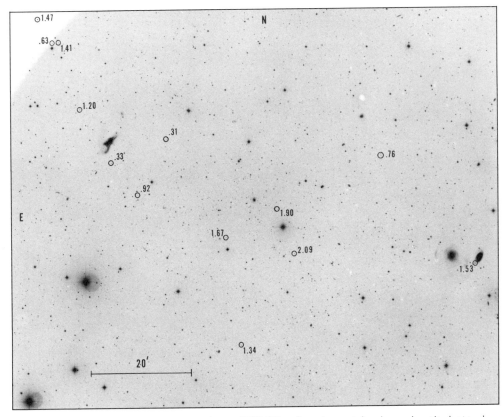

Figure 4-9. All quasars brighter than 19th apparent magnitude around NGC 520 are shown, from two independent searches within the pictured area (from Arp and Duhalde 1985). Is there a line of quasars going through NGC 520? Why did referees and editors of two major journals refuse publication of this result?

background. It reaches 15 times expected density, about the same factor that we have encountered for excess density around galaxies previously discussed. Since all members of the line are undeniably quasars, in order to make the line "go away," one would have to discover many more quasars which would further increase the density above its already strong excess.

The next piece of the puzzle fell in place, as the X-ray astronomers would say, serendipitously. I was scanning a list of targets which the Einstein X-ray observatory had observed. There, amongst a study entitled, "Normal Galaxies," was my old friend, NGC 520. How anyone could call NGC 520 a normal galaxy passes all understanding. But I understood

somewhat after I wrote the Harvard/Smithsonian Center to try to get a copy of the observations. It turned out they had been made by a new acquaintance, an astronomer who had just advanced his career with an article in the magazine called *The Sciences*, in which he had dismissed as trash anything I had ever uttered about redshifts. You can imagine that getting my hands on this X-ray map was not easy. I have never been able to compare it with other fields taken under the same conditions. But the single map I did get showed a lot of X-ray emission from the vicinity of NGC 520. It was apparent that whatever is producing the X-rays is elongated more or less along the line of the quasars. Figure 4-10 shows that the direction of the radio emission designated in

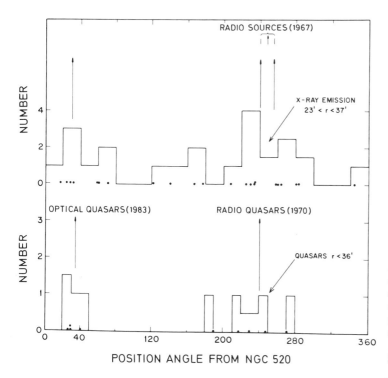

RADIO SOURCES (1967)

X-RAY EMISSION
23' < r < 37'

OPTICAL QUASARS (1983)   RADIO QUASARS (1970)

QUASARS r < 36'

NUMBER

POSITION ANGLE FROM NGC 520

Figure 4-10. The directions on the sky, from NGC 520, of the radio sources discovered in 1967 and the quasars discovered in 1970 (arrows). The X-ray material and additional quasars discovered in 1983 are represented by upper and lower histograms respectively.

1967 coincides very closely with the direction of the radio quasar line discovered in 1970, which then coincides with the direction of the quasar line discovered in 1983, which in turn coincides with the peak direction of X-ray emission discovered in 1983.

As in the previous case of NGC 1097, we have in NGC 520 strong evidence for quasars ejected in a jet and counterjet direction and for this ejection to be accompanied by X-ray and radio material. In NGC 520, no optical jets are visible, but on the other hand, the galaxy is much more explosively torn up than NGC 1097, suggesting a very violent event.

As to the interpretation of the structural appearance of NGC 520, there has been quite a fad in recent years to explain all asymmetrical galaxy forms as collisions or mergers. NGC 520 was interpreted in this fashion by my friends Alan Stockton and Francesco Bertola. The Armenian radio-astronomer Tovmassian, however, finds a single, compact radio source in the center of NGC 520 and favors the exploding-galaxy interpretation. My opinion is that the photographs taken with high-resolution telescopes do not permit the interpretation of NGC 520 as two galaxies. Finally, the radio, X-ray, and quasar activity we have just discussed supports the interpretation of NGC 520 as an active galaxy.

Two things have always bothered me about NGC 520. One is the large scale of the activity—the straight line of radio quasars stretches up to 7 degrees away from the galaxy—and the second is the relatively bright apparent-magnitudes of the quasars. The redshift of NGC 520 is about $cz_o = 2272$ km s^{-1}, which, on the cosmological hypothesis, gives a distance about twice as great as the Virgo supercluster center. I have occasionally had a little thought: Is NGC 520 really this distant or it is closer than its redshift would indicate? In Chapter 5, we see the most recent evidence that the galaxy may be closer.

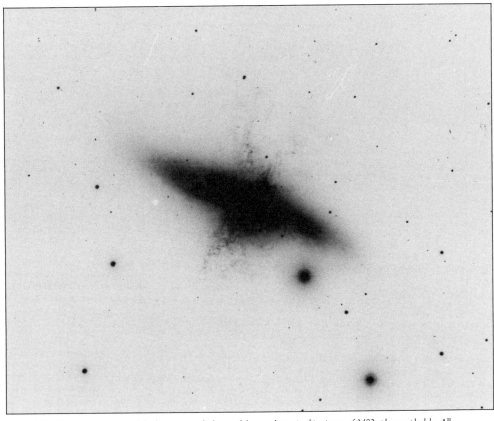

Figure 4-11. The filaments emitting light from gaseous hydrogen-alpha are shown in this picture of M82, photographed by Allan Sandage.

C. The Exploding Galaxy M82

This galaxy has always been one of the brightest and most peculiar known. (M stands for Charles Messier, the 18th century comet hunter.) In 1963, Allan Sandage took photographs of M82 revealing a twisted set of emission filaments emerging from either pole. M82 was interpreted as an exploding galaxy and became a prototype for objects in the universe exhibiting violent activity. (Some years later, there was an attempt to interpret M82 as a normal galaxy drifting through a cloud of dust, but in my opinion, the photographs patently rule that out. In addition, velocity spreads were later found in the gaseous filaments.) Sandage's photograph is shown in Figure 4-11.

We will come back to M82 in later chapters because it is such a key object. But for the present it suffices to say that the galaxy is a companion to M81, an even larger, apparently normal spiral which dominates the M81 group of galaxies. From the results of finding quasars near companion galaxies described in Chapter 2, I was predicting that quasars should be found near companions like M82. The system lay in a direction passing too near our own galactic plane, and hence was too crowded with stars for me to use the ultraviolet-excess technique for quasar-discovery. But about this time, Arthur Hoag had invented the grism (grating prism) which would give small spectra of faint objects in a field. Because Art had been a long and valued friend, I urged him to search for quasars around companion galaxies such as

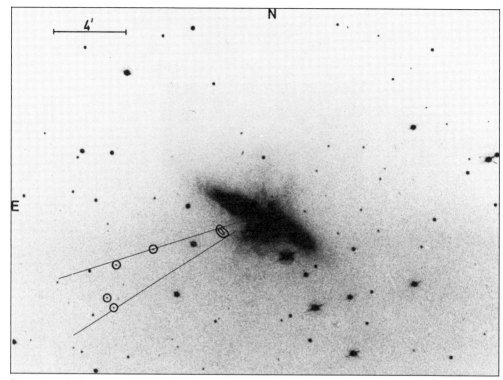

Figure 4-12. The four quasars which have been discovered near M82 are circled. The photograph is oxygen emission, showing the asymmetrical filaments which appear to be associated with the explosion. A radio source (slightly extended contours) appears to have been ejected along with the quasars from the "notch" in the southeast side of M82.

M82. I must say, the prospect of one of the genuinely good guys in astronomy making an important discovery with his genuinely important instrument pleased me also. But he insisted on observing so-called blank fields on the usual idea that this would give us the number density of quasars at the edge of the universe. (When it comes to the universe, one edge is about as good as another, hence the blank fields.) He was observing with Sandage one night and ran out of objects at the end of the night. To fill the time, they took a plate of M82. Can you imagine, they found three quasars about a galaxy diameter away to the southeast, an order of magnitude closer to each other than expected and all of about the same redshift!

Of all the quasars known, this is a unique grouping. It could hardly be a coincidence that they fall so close to the unique galaxy M82. It is natural, therefore, to trace the qua-

sars back to an origin in M82. As Figure 4-12 shows, they can be all contained within a cone emerging from the center of the galaxy. The opening angle of this cone is just about the observed opening angle in the ejection cones that we have seen emerging from the NGC 1097 and NGC 520. Moreover, in M82, this ejection cone emerges from the galaxy on the same side as the puff of forbidden oxygen emission. In fact, on the northern side of the [O II] emission there is a notch cut out, into which the origin of the ejection cone naturally fits. Finally, if we look back at Sandage's original hydrogen-alpha picture in Figure 4-11, we see that the most conspicuous absorption feature in the galaxy goes directly back to the center along the line of this postulated ejection cone (see also Arp 1980 in references in Appendix to this chapter).

The most recent developments concerning this system again come from X-rays. Fig-

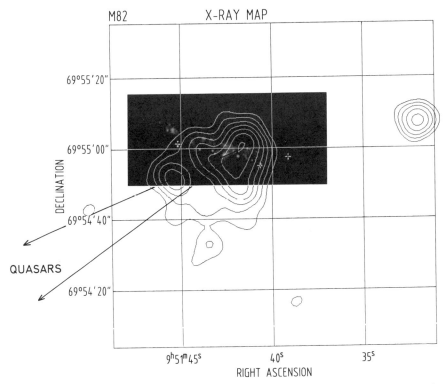

M82   X-RAY MAP

69°55'20"

69°55'00"

DECLINATION

69°54'40"

QUASARS

69°54'20"

9ʰ51ᵐ45ˢ   40ˢ   35ˢ

RIGHT ASCENSION

Figure 4-13. The radio map (photographed) of M82, with line contours of X-ray emission superposed. From Kronberg, Biermann, and Schwab. See chapter 9 for further discussion of X-ray emission.

ure 4-13 shows an X-ray map superposed on a radio map of the system. The compact, variable radio sources in a line down the spine of the galaxy are very peculiar, but the most significant result for our purposes is that the X-ray material is again over on the southeast side of M82 and, in fact, extends out generally along the direction of the ejection cone which we had identified several years previously from the quasar and morphological data. Added to the association evidence for the quasars, this correspondence of detailed X-ray and morphological evidence with the quasar alignment would indicate in this one case alone that the association of the quasars cannot be accidental.

Radio ejection? Of course. When J. J. Condon was observing a number of bright galaxies with the Very Large Array telescope, he found an unusual radio source just to the southeast of M82. As is customary in extragalactic astronomy, this observation would not

be related to any other unorthodox results which had been previously known. But, as Figure 4-12 shows, the patch of radio emission fits exactly into the quasar ejection cone just as it emerges from the explosive center of M82.

To summarize the results of this chapter, I would say that we have analyzed over many years and in great detail, three of the galaxies with the best evidence for explosive, ejecting behavior. In each of these cases we have found very strong statistical evidence for density enhancements of quasars near these galaxies. In all three cases alignments of quasars towards the centers of these disturbed galaxies exist that can hardly have occurred by chance. Connected with these alignments we find evidence for ejection of radio material and X-ray material. There does not seem to me to be much doubt, in just these cases alone, and even without the evidence from the first three chapters, that quasars arise from some kind of ejection process within galaxies.

Appendix to Chapter 4

1984, Arp. H., Wolstencroft, R. D., and He, X. T. Astrophys. Journ., 285. p. 44.

This is the latest paper on NGC 1097 and contains references to earlier work. NGC 1097 is also discussed below.

1983, Arp, H. in "Liège Symposium on Quasars and Gravitational Lenses," Institut d'Astrophysique. Universite de Liege, June 1983, Paper 47.

A number of results on "Groups, Concentrations, and Associations of Quasars," appear in the proceedings of this conference which are not published elsewhere. Discussion recorded at the end of this paper includes some obviously inaccurate statements about quasars of redshift near $z = 1$ containing only one visible emission line in their spectrum and selection of quasars near NGC 520.

1980, Arp, H., Annals of the New York Academy of Science, Vol. 336, pages 94-112.

This is the "Texas Symposium" in Munich. Results for association of quasars with galaxies, particularly with companion galaxies, are reviewed to that date. The evidence for an ejection cone of quasars from M82 is discussed only in this publication. The fourth quasar southeast of M82 is shown in *Astrophys Journ., 271, p. 479.*

1983, Condon, J.J., Astrophys. Journ., Supp., 53, p. 459.

Radio observations of M82.

1985, Arp, H. and Duhalde, O., Publ. Astron. Soc. Pac., 97, p. 1149.

Observations of quasars near NGC 520.

DISTRIBUTION 5
OF QUASARS
IN SPACE

The conventional view of quasars is that they are normal galaxies which have, for some reason, superluminous nuclei which enable them to be seen at great distances in the universe. But if quasars really were these kinds of galaxies, we should expect to see them clumping into the clusters or superclusters that characterize the distribution of galaxies on the largest scales. Attempts have been made to relate some quasars with faint, adjacent galaxies of the same redshift. But no conspicuous clusters are evident. Moreover, it is completely clear that we do not see clusters or groups of quasars all having closely the same redshift. The conclusion forced on the conventional believers is that quasars are so rare that we seldom see a cluster of galaxies with one; that is, far less than one quasar exists per average supercluster.

But if we look around the quasars we do see, to a faint enough level, we should see the galaxies that accompany them in their clusters and superclusters. Wide-field Schmidt telescopes, since the invention of high-detectivity emulsions, can routinely register galaxies to a limiting apparent magnitude fainter than 23. That corresponds to a redshift for a

normal galaxy of at least $z \approx 0.5$.

We should be able to easily see faint, rich clusters of galaxies around quasars out to this redshift and beyond. We do not. (You can believe that if we did we would have heard an enormous amount about it!) Clearly, this is an outstanding violation of the cosmological assumptions.

The only way to place the quasars into clusters, where they "belong", is to move them in much closer than their redshift distance. In fact, throughout this book we shall see that if the objects with anomalous redshifts are assigned closer distances they join nearby groups and clusters of galaxies. This is the way the universe is observed to be structured. But if these objects are left out at their putative redshift distances they are left hanging isolated in space.

Of course an inverse investigation could be made. The faintest, richest superclusters in the sky could be identified and the area which they define summed. On the cosmological assumption these areas should contain most of the known quasars of the same redshift. My impression, from what I have seen of the distribution of faint galaxies with re-

TABLE 5-1
Quasars in Dense Groups

No. Group Name	Redshifts of Quasars						Area (sq. deg.)	Factor of Density Over Average
	z_1	z_2	z_3	z_4	z_5	z_6		
1. Hazard 1146 + 1112 (~2° SE of NGC 3810)	1.01	1.01	1.10	0.86	2.12	—	0.014	60
2. NGC 450 SW (~2° SW of NGC 450)	0.955	0.960	0.69	1.23	1.89	—	0.013	64
3. NGC 2639 SE (~30' SE of NGC 2639)	1.18	1.11	1.52	(0.78)	—	—	0.013	51
4. NGC 1097 NE (within 24' of NGC 1097)	3.1	0.53	1.00	0.34	0.89	(1.1)	0.04–0.02	21-50
5. NGC 520 (within 28' of NGC 520)	0.33	0.92	1.20	0.63	1.41	1.47	0.05	60

spect to quasars, is that this test would fail spectacularly and that this is why the researchers of cosmological persuasion have not performed it.

On the other hand, examining the distribution of quasars on the sky does reveal conspicuous clumps and groups of quasars. The trouble is that the quasars within each group have dissimilar, or only moderately similar, redshifts. If these groupings are real, and if the redshifts were distance indicators, each group, with its range of redshift, would represent an elongated "finger" of quasars pointing just at our position in space. The Copernican principle, namely that the odds are overwhelmingly against our occupying a special position in the universe, would then require that the redshifts of these quasars did not indicate their distances. The fingers pointing at us are telling us our assumptions about redshift are foolish.

A. The Densest Groups of Quasars

In order to investigate this question of grouping of quasars without prejudice as to redshift, I list in Table 5-1 the densest groups of four or more quasars that I have encountered in my 20 years of quasar research. Some of these groups, such as the ones shown in Figures 5-1 and 5-2 are so compact and isolated that there could be no question that they are a physically associated group of quasars. I make no attempt to prove this statistically in the sense of computing the chance of finding these configurations in a sample of random quasars in the sky. Since most astronomers pay no attention to proofs that quasars are local anyway, I might as well present an easy proof rather than a hard one. Instead of doing complicated statistics on heterogeneous searches, I simply reason that if the five dens-

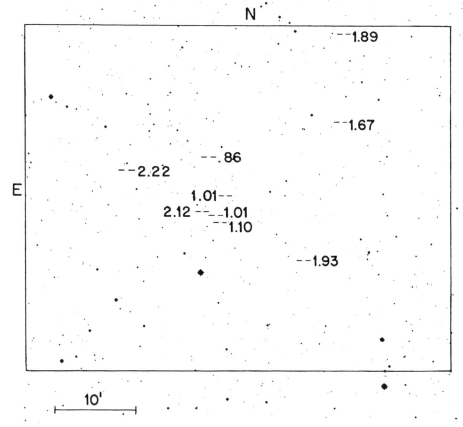

Figure 5-1. Identification of all quasars within an area located about 2° SE of NGC 3810, found from objective-prism spectral searches by Arp and Hazard. Redshifts are written next to position of quasars.

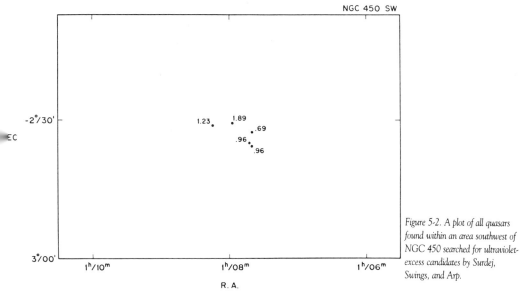

Figure 5-2. A plot of all quasars found within an area southwest of NGC 450 searched for ultraviolet-excess candidates by Surdej, Swings, and Arp.

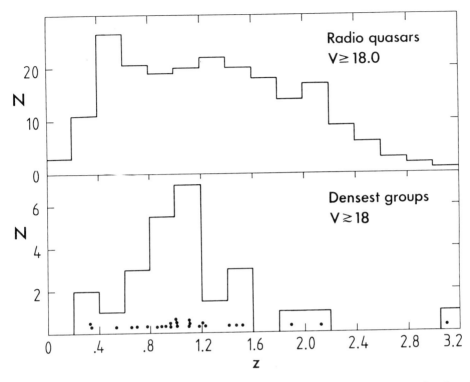

Figure 5-3. The distribution of quasar redshifts for the densest groups compared to the distribution of redshifts for radio quasars from all over the sky.

est groups in Table 5-1 were random associations, they should have the same properties as the average quasars in the sky. They have, in fact, outstandingly different properties. For example, Figure 5-3 and Table 5-1 reveal that there is a clear preference for redshifts between $0.8 < z < 1.2$, whereas radio quasars from all over the sky are rather evenly distributed between $0.4 < z < 2.2$.

There is also a tendency to find pairs of quasars within each group. (Pairing tendencies for quasars are discussed further in the Appendix to this chapter.) On the average, the pairs within these dense groups are separated by only 4.6 arcmin on the sky and only 0.07 in redshift. The chance of finding such pairs by chance within the general population of quasars is only about 10^{-3} per pair. Yet we find eight such pairs in the five dense groups. Even allowing for the fact that these are selected dense groupings of quasars, there is clearly a significant physical association of pairs. Their average difference in redshift of $\triangle z = 0.07$, however, translates to a velocity difference of 21,000 km s^{-1}, a clearly impossible value for objects belonging, on the cosmological interpretation, to the same cluster or supercluster of galaxies.*

The physical reality of these dense groups destroys the possibility that quasars are at

*The one pair among the 26 quasars listed in Table 5-1 which has very closely similar redshifts was recently pounced upon by advocates of conventional quasar distances. They proclaimed this pair to be the result of a gravitational lens of enormous and unprecedented mass sitting invisibly out somewhere in this direction in the universe (*Nature 321*, p. 142, 1986). Embarrassingly enough, further observations revealed almost immediately that the spectra were in fact enough different so that the quasars had to be two separate, albeit quite similar quasars. This is just the pairing tendency evident in the quasars discussed in this chapter and evident in the compact, excess-redshift ejecta of active galaxies discussed in following chapters. The above, widely publicized incident of marvelous discovery and almost instant refutation, however, underscores two points: (1) no result in the field is absurd enough to provoke re-examination of basic assumptions, and (2) selecting one aspect of data which supports a hypothesis and ignoring other aspects which contradict that hypothesis is a form of "altering data".

their redshift distances, because, as just explained, the redshift range of the associated quasars is too large by a wide margin. A typical cluster of galaxies near redshift $z = 1$ would have redshifts ranging, at most, between $0.99 < z < 1.01$.

But at the same time, the existence of these groups is the key that unlocks a more detailed understanding of the puzzling data on quasars. The reason that it is such a key is that it allows us to ask a crucial question. (It might be said that the most difficult part of research is not to get the right answer, but to ask the right question.) The question is:

"Why do the densest groups of quasars have redshifts near $z = 1$?"

B. The Intrinsic Luminosities of Quasars of Different Redshifts

One obvious answer to the question of why the densest groups of quasars have $z \approx 1$ is: "The luminosity of quasars with $z = 1$ is greater than the luminosity of quasars of other redshifts." In that case, the $z = 1$ quasars could be seen at a greater distance, where the scale of their separation appears smaller and the groups therefore appear denser.

Can this be tested? Yes, a straightforward way to test this is by plotting the apparent magnitudes versus the redshifts for all the various groups of quasars that I have, over the years, come to believe are physically associated. This has been done in Figure 5-4. For these quasars at the same distance, those of brightest apparent magnitude must be the most intrinsically luminous. We realize from the upper-left-hand panel alone in Figure 5-4 what we should have seen in 1970, that the quasars near $z = 1$ are the intrinsically brightest quasars. (Actually, this point was first stressed in my contribution to the 1972 Krakow and Australian symposia referenced in the Appendix of Chapter 2.) In that same Chapter 2, we discussed the 1970 paper in the *Astronomical Journal* which showed that the

optically faint radio quasars in the North Galactic Hemisphere (NGH radio quasars in Fig. 5-4) are associated with the Virgo cluster of galaxies, i.e., the center of our Local Supercluster. This 1970 study is now translated into the upper-left panel in Figure 5-4 where we see that the brightest quasars belonging to the Virgo cluster are concentrated in redshift near $z \sim 1$. There are almost no quasars near $z \sim 2$. Presumably, they are too faint in apparent magnitude to be observed in Virgo!

In contrast, the same sample of quasars in the opposite direction of the sky (SGH radio quasars) show a strong concentration near redshifts $z \sim 2$. This represents *gross* differences in the quasar distribution within a complete and homogeneous quasar sample over the sky. On the cosmological interpretation of quasars this would require an enormous violation of the usually assumed cosmological principle that on large distance scale the universe is homogeneous. It is astonishing that this clear evidence contradicting the cosmological assumption has lain ignored and uninvestigated for over 15 years!

To return to the luminosity-redshift relation for quasars, we can easily draw in the line satisfying the average values for the NGH radio quasars in Figure 5-4. This "roof-shaped" relation is shown as a line in the two panels in the middle of the figure. Even though this roof-shaped line is derived from the NGH quasars in the upper-left-hand panel, we do not draw it in that panel in order to avoid prejudicing the eye with the line. One can thereby see that the points just representing the NGH quasars by themselves clearly define the adopted relation. (A roof-shaped relation implies that the quasars with redshift $z \approx 1$ are the intrinsically most luminous and that quasars with both lower and higher redshifts are less luminous.)

The fit of this luminosity-redshift relation to the quasars studied in the NGC 1097 field is shown in the upper middle panel of Figure 5-4. From the study of NGC 1097 discussed

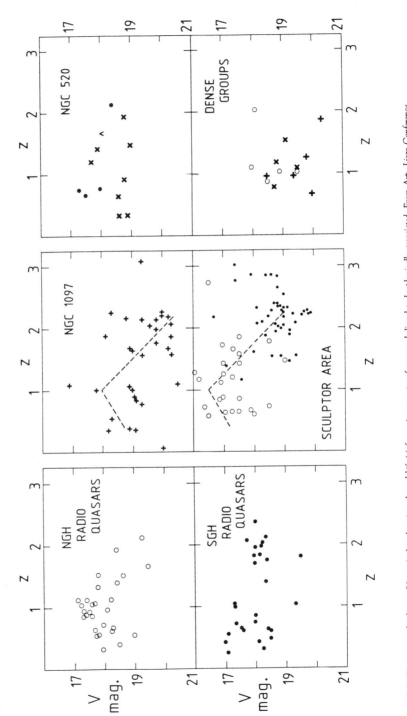

Figure 5.4. The apparent brightness (V mag.) plotted against the redshift (z) for various groups of quasars believed to be physically associated. From Arp, Liège Conference.

in Chapter 4, we would expect 12 to 15 more quasars than expected from average background to represent the quasars actually physically associated with this jet galaxy. Possibly some of the brighter and certainly some of the fainter quasars represent projected foreground and background objects. In that case, we find just about a dozen or so quasars which outline the expected relation fairly well.

The other association of quasars discussed in Chapter 4 was with the galaxy NGC 520. Those quasars are shown in the upper-right-hand panel of Figure 5-4. They also appear to outline a roof relation quite well, particularly the brighter envelope of points. The actual line has not been drawn in the NGC 520 panel because that would commit us to a zero point for the system, i.e., it would say that we actually believe a certain relative distance for the system. Later, we will encounter confirmatory evidence for NGC 520 being a member of the Local Group of galaxies despite the rather large redshift of the central, disturbed galaxy ($z = 2200$ km s^{-1}). (We are actually using *quasars* here as distance indicators for peculiar galaxies!)

Quasars from three of the densest groups on the sky as discussed earlier and illustrated in Figures 5-1 and 5-2 are now plotted in the bottom right panel of Figure 5-4. It is evident that they concentrate around redshift $z \approx 1$ as if they were more distant objects that had just poked above the limiting threshold of discovery at $V = 19$th to 20th magnitude.

Next we come to an area in the sky near the constellation of Sculptor. Later in this chapter, we discuss the evidence for a large physical association of quasars in this area. In the lower middle panel of Figure 5-4 we plot the many high-redshift quasars in this group found by objective-prism techniques (filled circles). In order to get an idea where the brighter quasars in this area fall we also plot radio quasars (open circles). The quasars in this region could therefore satisfy a roof relation moved rather close to us—that is, a relation involving bright apparent magnitude quasars. This panel cannot be taken too rigorously because the size of the regions have been arbitrarily adjusted. But the Sculptor region will be considered in much more detail later and the association of the quasars with the nearby Sculptor group galaxies justified in detail.

The final panel in the lower left of Figure 5-4 shows that in the South Galactic Hemisphere (SGH radio quasars) the quasars might be fitted by the brightest (nearest to us) roof-relation of all. The direction of these quasars defines essentially the direction of the Local Group of galaxies, the nearest galaxies to us.

The establishment and verification of this luminosity-redshift relation for quasars forces us to consider the surprising conclusion that the highest redshift quasars ($z \sim 2$), instead of being the most luminous objects in the universe as has been heretofore supposed, are actually the least intrinsically luminous quasars. This is a startling development but it enables us to pose the most crucial question of all. It is:

"If the quasars with redshifts near $z \approx 2$ have the intrinsically lowest luminosities, then those that have the brightest apparent magnitudes are the closest quasars to us in space. Where are *they* located on the sky?"

C. Quasars in the Local Group of Galaxies

The answer to the question of where the lowest-luminosity quasars are located in the sky breaks open the box of contradictory inferences into which the establishment has so far succeeded in locking this issue. Figure 5-5 shows the plot of all apparently bright radio quasars, found from radio surveys over the sky, with redshift near $z \sim 2$. It is immediately obvious that there are three to four times as many of these high-z quasars on the half of the sky toward the Local Group of galaxies than there are in the side of the sky toward the more distant Virgo supercluster. There really is no way around this result. It requires that many of the known quasars come from galaxies that are among the closest to us. Moreover, this one group of quasars and nearby galaxies spreads over areas of the order of one-third of the visible sky. In some sense, we are imbedded in the edge of the Local Group and would expect to see some of it, at least thinly, in all directions. Since quasars with smaller redshifts are generally intrinsically more luminous and can be seen in more distant, apparently smaller groups in different directions on the sky, and since all this depends on the apparent magnitude level we are looking at, it is not surprising that conventional, nondiscriminating analyses can make, and have made, almost any statement they please about quasar distribution on the sky. In contrast, the lesson we have learned so far in this section is that the intrinsic luminosity of a quasar depends on its redshift, and that at any given redshift, its apparent magnitude depends on its distance.

This is strong stuff. Even though I feel it follows ineluctably from the observational evidence, it is still necessary, in the old-time scientific spirit, to test it against all the evidence we can get our hands on. The first test we make is to look more closely at that concentration of quasars in the direction of the center of the Local Group. Figure 5-6 shows a region of the sky more directly centered on the Local Group. There we see an obvious line of quasars extending from mid-upper left to lower right. The line originates from the Local Group companion galaxy, M33! We saw in Chapter 2 that, statistically, quasars tend to be associated with companion galaxies, ostensibly because companion galaxies are a younger and more active variety of galaxies. M33 is the famous spiral in Triangulum with spiral arms composed of young, blue stars and glowing hydrogen gas. It is the most conspicuous

companion to the dominant galaxy in our own Local Group.

M33 is the nearest spiral galaxy of this type to us. Now, we see the nearest quasars to us emerging on a line from this object. I really do not know which is the more exciting, seeing this much maligned idea of local quasars exonerated so dramatically, or the shock of confronting this new and greater mystery of what the quasars are and how they originate from M33.

There is, of course, the naturally following question of what else is associated with M33. A similar graphical analysis to that of Figures 5-5 and 5-6 shows that there is also a concentration of low-redshift ($0.27 < z < 0.47$) quasars near M33. But they are all brighter, about 2 magnitudes brighter, than the high-redshift quasars that we have just seen associated with M33. Now we check against the "roof" relation derived from Figure 5-4 and see that the luminosities of these lower-redshift quasars are required to be just about 2 magnitudes brighter! (See Fig. 5-8.) So the quasars found associated with M33 confirm this relation.

Not only do we see quasars of low redshift in this region southeast of M33, but we also see certain radio galaxies of the same redshift. Since many of the low-redshift quasars have fuzzy edges when closely inspected on good photographs, these radio galaxies, which have somewhat fuzzier edges, are physically similar and form a continuous class. (The naive insistence of the cosmological group that any spot in the sky that is fuzzy has to be at its redshift distance will be discussed in forthcoming chapters.) But as Figure 5-7 shows, the exciting fact about the distribution of low-redshift quasars and radio galaxies is that not only do they also form an elongated group southwest of M33, but also that the direction of that elongation is rotated slightly counterclockwise from the line of high-redshift quasars!

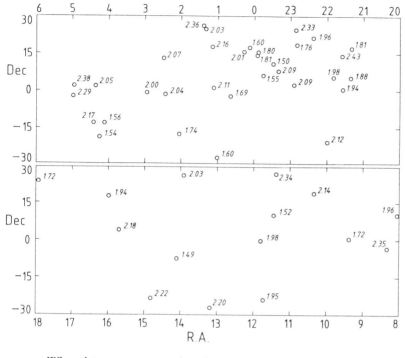

Figure 5-5. A plot of high-redshift quasars all around the sky. Redshifts are written next to the position of each quasar. The center of the Local Group of galaxies is at roughly R.A. = 0ʰ 40ᵐ, Dec. = +41°

What this must mean is that the quasars are indeed ejected from galaxies, as we saw in Chapters 3 and 4, but that ejection direction does not stay fixed in space. As a function of time we would expect it to rotate because the ejecting galaxies rotate. Quasars ejected in one direction should also be older than quasars ejected in a later direction. This implies that what are now the lower-redshift quasars were ejected earlier and that as time progressed they became more luminous and evolved from high redshift to their present low redshift. That is, the quasars became more like peculiar, high-redshift, companion galaxies. This represents the most provocative direction in which to follow up these results, as will be discussed later. But at this point I would like to cement absolutely the

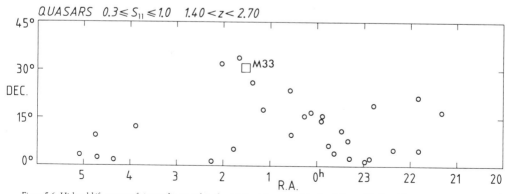

Figure 5-6. High-redshift quasars of given radio strength in the vicinity of the center of the Local Group. The Local Group companion galaxy, M33, is shown by an open square. From Arp, Journal of Astrophysics and Astronomy (1984).

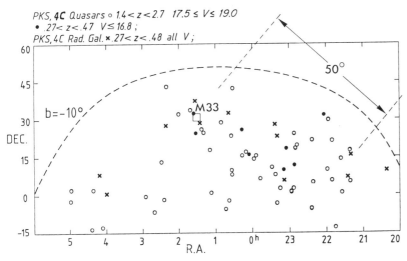

Figure 5-7. The distribution toward M33 of high-redshift quasars (open circles), bright, low-redshift quasars (filled circles) and low-redshift radio galaxies (crosses).

unique nature of the distribution of the quasars around M33 and their association with M33.

First of all, there is the point about the reality of the concentration and alignment of quasars southeast of M33. Accepting its reality, as we shall see in a moment, leads to disaster for the conventional viewpoint. Given this end result, the usual procedure for the establishment, as in the precedent of previous events, would be to perform a statistical analysis on the distribution in which boundary assumptions would be adjusted until they yielded a nonsignificant result. Fortunately, this has been forestalled by a sophisticated and thorough statistical analysis performed by the astrophysicists J. Narlikar and K. Subramanian at the Tata Institute in Bombay, India. They show that the quasars in Figures 5-5 are significant concentrations, with probabilities only about 10^{-4} of being random distributions, and that the quasars are also significantly aligned by the same large factors of significance. This is an important piece of mathematical analysis, but for myself, and I suspect for many readers, simply the visual evidence in Figures 5-5 and 5-6 demonstrate quite forcefully that there is a real alignment of quasars emerging to the southwest from M33.

In order to see exactly what this quasar alignment consists of, we outline the greatest concentration of high-redshift quasars in the vicinity of M33. We then display all the radio quasars present inside this region in the apparent magnitude-redshift diagram in the top panel of Figure 5-8. We use radio quasars throughout because they are drawn from radio surveys, which are generally homogeneous all over the sky at any given declination. In the bottom diagram we display all the radio quasars in a much larger comparison area in the opposite direction in the sky (the Virgo supercluster region). We see that the distributions are completely different. The most important difference is the large clump of high-redshift quasars which are relatively bright in apparent magnitude (around V ≈ 18 mag.) which are present southwest of M33 but are essentially absent in the opposite quadrant of the sky. These high-redshift quasars are simply the closest large group of quasars to us, associated with the Local Group galaxy M33.

Given the reality and uniqueness of the quasar alignment with M33, the last remaining escape for the cosmological adherents is to claim, "selection effects." The disproof of this possibility is very cutting. The reason is

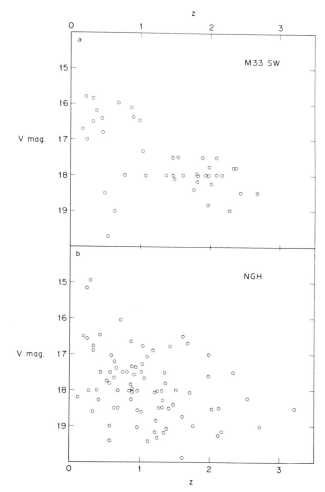

Figure 5-8. Inside the area
southwest of M33 are shown all
radio quasars in an apparent
magnitude-redshift diagram. Below is shown a larger comparison area in the opposite direction
of the sky.

that all the quasars we are dealing with are undeniably real quasars—spectra which identify the redshifts exist for all of them. Therefore the only possible way to make the concentration southwest of M33 disappear is to discover many more high-redshift radio quasars in other directions all over the sky.

But it is preposterous to suppose that only radio quasars of high redshift were selectively *not* observed in other regions of the sky.

Yet this is what the conventional interpretation must claim in order to save the situation. It should be made very clear that *they* have the responsibility of producing, and publishing, the spectra of these missing quasars near $z \sim 2$, either that or admit their distribution is anomalous. If they admit the latter they will have a grotesque inhomogeneity on the largest scale of the universe pointing at the observer (because the inhomogeneity contains a range of redshifts around $z \sim 2$). They would also have to ascribe the alignment with M33 as an accident.

Two further interesting comments can be made about Figure 5-8: One is that the quasars in the top panel are all very bright in apparent magnitude. That is as required by their belonging to a galaxy as close to us in space as M33. In fact, the "roof" relation derived from the analysis earlier in this chapter is confirmed in Figure 5-8 by the fact that the quasars of redshift $z \sim 1$ or less average about two magnitudes intrinsically brighter than quasars around $z \approx 2$. The other interesting feature of the quasars southwest of M33 is that very few quasars of faint apparent magnitude appear in this area. It is as if we were seeing a cloud at the distance of the Local Group of galaxies and then a relative void beyond.

The "cloud" distribution is a necessity on both the cosmological and local interpretation of quasars. That is because Olbers' paradox would demand an infinite sky brightness if they were not in clouds. (Olbers merely pointed out that a uniform distribution of luminous objects extending to an indefinitely large radius in space would necessarily lead to an indefinitely bright sky instead of the dark night sky we observe.) In the cosmological interpretation, the catastrophe is avoided by invoking "evolution" of quasars. That is, beyond a certain distance, the conventional viewpoint resorts to simply turning out the quasars (saying they are too young to have formed). So, they are dealing with a limited cloud, but one of very large dimensions. The local interpretation, we see, simply has smaller dimensions to its clouds of quasars. Since these local quasars are generally less luminous than the galaxies they are grouped with, they avoid an infinite sky-brightness in the same natural way as do the groups and clusters of galaxies to which they belong.

But there is an added fillip to this necessary cloud picture:

Fred Hoyle pointed out an absolute mathematical disproof of the cosmological nature of quasars. Mathematically he showed that in order to reproduce, on the cosmological assumption, the observed numbers of quasars as a function of redshift, their luminosity function must be very steep. (That is, at a given distance, or redshift, the number of quasars must increase rapidly as their luminosity decreases.) All the conventional analyses indeed require this very steep luminosity function. Yet as Hoyle points out, the observations strongly violate this requirement. You

can see a dramatic example of this in the top of Figure 5-8. Between redshifts $0.2 \leq z \leq 1.0$ there are a number of quasars between apparent magnitude $16 \leq V \leq 17$ mag. If the conventional luminosity function were really valid, then we should observe *ten times* as many quasars in the redshift interval between $18.5 \leq V \leq 19.5$ mag. Actually, we observe practically none. There could scarcely be a more clear-cut observational contradiction of the cosmological requirement. It may or may not be hard to believe, but many astronomical research centers do not even have the Hoyle publication. One center where I brought it to their attention made the reply that: "Well, the mathematics are correct but the observations are not good enough to test the claim."

It would be a marvelous confirmation of what we have learned about quasars in the Local Group if we could look at the next most distant group of galaxies and observe something like the same phenomena at a correspondingly smaller scale and fainter apparent magnitude. That opportunity is presented to us by a group of galaxies located in the constellation of Sculptor.

D. The Sculptor Group of Galaxies

A group of galaxies in the southern hemisphere of the sky lies roughly 2-3 times farther from us than the Local Group galaxies such as M33 which we have just discussed. Two dominant galaxies define the Sculptor Group. One is the impressive spiral galaxy NGC 300, which is of much the same type as M33 yet still close enough to see distance-indicating Cepheid variable stars in the arms. The other, NGC 55, has comparable size but more irregular shape. Now an extraordinary stroke of good luck occurred when two astronomers at the U.S. National Observatory in Chile, decided to observe a sample of quasars. They picked a declination zone that ran high overhead for them (Dec = $-40°$) and observed a

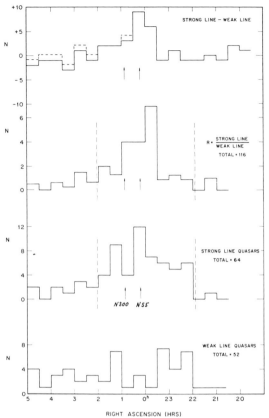

Figure 5-9. The numbers of objective prism quasars in the Dec = −40° zone. Note that the proportion of strong-line quasars rises just at the position of the Sculptor group galaxies NGC 300 and NGC 55.

long, narrow strip of sky, 5 degrees wide, running from west to east. The good luck was that this strip runs right across our Sculptor galaxies NGC 300 and NGC 55. The beginning and the end of the strip lie outside the Sculptor group and can be used to compare to the results in the center of the strip.

An uncomfortable result became apparent as soon as they plotted their results. A good many more quasars were found in the center of the strip than at the edges. Since these two astronomers accepted unquestioningly that the quasars were out at the far reaches of the universe, this result obviously could not be correct. Therefore, after the fact, they decided that the photographic emulsions they had used were less sensitive on either end of the strip than they were in the middle of the strip!

This was duly published and accepted.

But I noticed that the quasars at the ends of the strip contained proportionally more "weak-lined" quasars. That is, the emission lines identifying them as quasars were fainter and they were consequently more difficult to discover. If the photographic emulsions were really less sensitive at the ends of the strip, then a proportionally smaller number of these quasars should have been found rather than a larger number. When I tried to publish this result in the British journal, *Monthly Notices of the Royal Astronomical Society,* it was sent to one of the original two authors to referee. Needless to say, it was not published. It was almost stopped again when I sent a short article to *Nature,* but, thanks to the last-minute intervention of an editor, it finally appeared. The diagram shown in Figure 5-9 is from that article and shows how the concentration of strong-line quasars rises dramatically at just

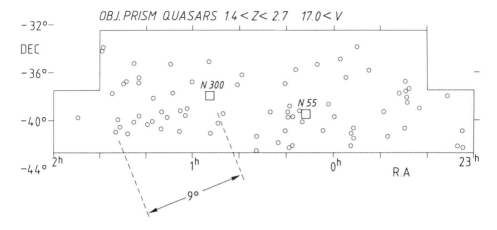

Figure 5-10. Plot of the high-redshift quasars in the region of the Sculptor group galaxies.

the position of the Sculptor group galaxies, NGC 300 and NGC 55. It is interesting that we have here more than just a concentration of quasars in this region. We have a concentration of a particular kind of quasar. (The Appendix to Chapter 1 references articles which discuss factors of 10 density discrepancies across this region.)

I was able to measure more quasars north of the Dec = –40° strip, and thus extend the areas of homogenous quasar discovery to the next strip around NGC 300 and NGC 55. These results are shown in Figure 5-10. The quasars in this entire area are now seen to have a very interesting distribution. Of course, there is the general excess of quasars demonstrated by Figure 5-9. But in addition these excess quasars tend to group around the major galaxies, NGC 300 and NGC 55.

The densest distribution in Figure 5-10 forms a line southeast of NGC 300 about 9 degrees long. In Figure 5-7 we saw a similar elongated alignment of quasars emerging from M33. Of course, the line from M33 was about 5 times longer in angular extent, but M33 is less than half as distant. These lines also must have arbitrary projection angles in space. Finally we can check the apparent magnitudes of the quasars in these lines, and

as Figure 5-11 shows, the NGC 300 quasars are just about 1.5 magnitudes (a factor of two in distance) fainter. Therefore we see that in both the closest and next closest groups of galaxies to us in space we identify elongated distributions of quasars emerging from the major spiral galaxies in each group. Moreover, the scale of the distribution on the sky and apparent magnitude of the quasars supports the known fact that the second group of galaxies is just about twice as distant. Of course, lines of quasars are exactly what we observed in the ejecting galaxies NGC 1097, NGC 520, and M82 in the preceding chapter.

E. The Quasars Belonging to M82

It is more than interesting now to re-examine the third most distant group of galaxies from us. That is the M81 group at about 1 magnitude greater distance modulus than NGC 300. The major active companion in that group, M82, was found to have an "ejection cone" of three quasars with redshifts around z ~ 2 emerging from it (Chapter 4). This is the beginning of a line, or elongated distribution.

These quasars are very faint, between 20th and 21st magnitude, as shown in Figure

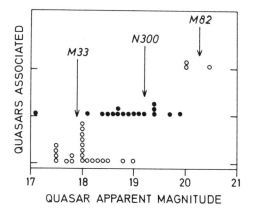

Figure 5-11. Comparison of apparent magnitudes of high redshift quasars in M33, NGC 300, and M82 lines. See Arp (1984, Fig. 4) for details. Note that the high redshift quasars associated with the most distant of the three galaxies, M82, are almost at the discovery limit.

5-11. So we apparently have a glimpse, at apparent magnitudes just above the plate limit, of a similar line of high-redshift quasars emerging from an active galaxy in also the third most distant group of galaxies. Figure 5-11 demonstrates that the apparent brightness of their associated quasars scales accurately as would be required of galaxies at these three different distances.

Summary

What we have done in this chapter is to account for large numbers of quasars. Referring to the numerous quasars mentioned in the beginning of the chapter that were not obviously associated with any galaxy, it turns out now that many are, in fact, associated with galaxies—it is just that the galaxies are so close that the associations stretch over large areas of the sky. It also turns out that the high-redshift quasars around $z \approx 2$ are not generally seen beyond the relatively nearby M81 group. That means that we have high-redshift quasars which belong to M33, and possibly to other members of the Local Group, projected over large areas of the sky, probably quasars that belong to our own galaxy which could be projected in almost any direction in the sky, plus various quasars that are contributed by more distant galaxies and groups like Sculptor and M81.

It will require some study and discrimination to sort out which quasars belong to which groups; possibly, in a number of cases, we can never be completely certain. The picture is further complicated when we consider quasars with redshifts around $z = 1$. These are intrinsically brighter and can be seen at greater distances. Therefore they contribute some very bright apparent magnitude quasars which belong to extended nearby groups and in addition contribute fainter, smaller-scale groupings. But the smaller-scale groupings appear in regions of the sky which do not have much relation to the nearby, larger groupings.

What is clearly needed now are careful, homogeneous quasar searches with various techniques to uniform limiting magnitudes all over the sky. Then detailed interpretation can be made. This is the necessary, hard scientific work that should have been undertaken long ago. It is simply irresponsible to say, "I know all the important things about the universe—I do not have to study it. I need only to take a sample here and a sample there and announce that my model is now correct to several decimal places." This approach reminds us of the blind men feeling the elephant. One feels the leg and says an elephant is a tree, another feels the trunk and says it is a snake. In current extragalactic astronomy, one group has gone a step further by trying to eliminate all the others and to be left proudly waving the tail and proclaiming, "There is no uncertainty about the answer now."

Before we go on to the next chapter, however, we have to face a difficult and challenging problem. The problem is, namely, that associating the quasars with nearby galaxies means that their redshifts cannot be due to the Doppler effect of a recession velocity at great distances in the universe. Some other explanation for the high redshifts of the quasars must exist. What this explanation is, is a matter of spirited debate, as it should be, among that small band of astronomers who believe in the noncosmological redshifts of quasars. We will come to this animated discussion in a few chapters, but before that I would like to talk about nonvelocity redshifts in galaxies. That's right, galaxies. The reason for this is that quasars are small, mysterious objects that invite speculative theories. Perhaps they are redshifted by a strong gravitational field, perhaps by high ejection velocities, perhaps by robbing the photons of their energy by some scattering process. Some theorists have been intrigued with the idea that quasars are distant objects which are gravitationally lensed, and amplified in brightness, by galaxies near their light path. But evidence points to the fact that galaxies can also have nonvelocity redshifts. If this is true it presents us with objects we know vastly more about. We can actually study rotation, dynamics, and chemical composition of the constitutent stars in many galaxies. How could an entire galaxy have a nonvelocity redshift? The answer to this may be even more far-reaching and staggering than the answer to the same question about quasars. And, if the more energetic, compact forms of galaxies can be shown to be physically continuous with quasars then the answer to the redshift riddle for quasars may be the same for quasars as for galaxies.

Appendix to Chapter 5

PAIRS OF QUASARS
    The tendency of quasars to pair has been obvious for a long time. In 1970(*Astron. Journ.* Vol. 75, p. 1), I pointed out a number of quasars which fell conspicuously closer to each other on the sky than average and had a number of properties such as apparent magnitude, radio properties, and redshifts which resembled each other more than one would expect for randomly occurring objects. Of course, the redshifts were, typically, enough different so that they would invalidate the cosmological redshift assumption if the quasars were actually physically associated. I remember, in the early days, Fred Hoyle discussing the obvious similarities between 3C286 and 3C287, two quasars close together in the sky. Today, it is impressive to run your eye down modern lists of quasars and see how many obvious pairs stand out.
    This phenomenon was quantitatively investigated by G. R. Burbidge, E. M. Burbidge, and S. L. O'Dell in 1974. They demonstrated, using only the few very close   quasar pairs known at the time, that the redshift differences could not be reconciled with redshifts indicative of distance. Poof! There went the cosmological hypothesis! Well, one would have thought so, but it was privately stated with calm assurance that this calculation did not count because the test was made after the quasars had been discovered. This is the old "a posteriori" argument which was now further deformed to say, "You cannot test any data that already exists." Undaunted? Well, I cannot say, but Burbidge and Narlikar nevertheless recently went on to make the calculation using all the quasars discovered *after* the time of their first analysis. They now obtain a probability ~ 10^{-4}, less than one chance in ten thousand that these pairs can be accidental (see references following).
    An illustration of how things work in this game was accidentally revealed to me shortly before this last Burbidge and Narlikar paper. An astronomer analyzing this quasar data found a disturbingly significant excess of these same pairs. He said, "Well, this is obviously a selection effect caused by astronomers looking in the vicinity of radio quasars for nonradio quasars." (Of course, these cases are minuscule in number and could be easily identified.) But as he "normalized out" this effect and sent his paper proclaiming another proof of the cosmological nature of quasars off for instant publication, he smiled at me and said, "Gee, Chip, I really would love to find some hard evidence for noncosmological quasars."
    The latest paper on this subject (European Southern Observatory Preprint No. 422) purports to refute the physical pairing of quasars of different redshift. But the analysis mixes physical groupings of widely different distances and hence widely different characteristic separations. Even so, close inspection of the graphical results shows consistently more close separations than expected. The effect would be even more conspicuous if the fitted line had been drawn accurately through the points representing large separation.

Redshift Periodicities in Different Groups of Quasars

Now that we have established the existence of different physical groups of quasars, we can take another, more illuminating look at the preferred values of quasar redshifts that are discussed toward the end of the first chapter. We saw there that the three quasars in NGC 1073 fit almost exactly the mean periodicity of all quasars taken as a whole. But other physical groups of quasars can have slightly different periodicites. Because the spacing between periods follows the rule that the intervals in the logarithm of $(1 + z)$ are constant ($\Delta (\log 1 + z) = $ const.), a group with a slightly different constant will have intervals which become progressively larger as larger redshifts are considered. An example of this is shown in Figure 5-12.

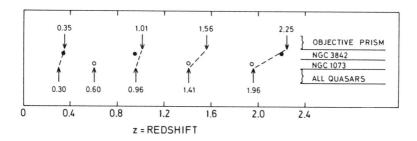

Figure 5-12. The preferred periods for all quasars as a whole are shown along the bottom of the strip. Preferred periods for the objective prism quasars (which are dominated by the Sculptor group quasars) are shown along the top. The points indicate how well the triplets of quasars discussed in Chapter 1 fit these preferred periods.

The quasars selected by objective prism searches (Box and Roeder, see Appendix to Chapter 1) are dominated by the large group of quasars associated with the Sculptor group of galaxies discussed earlier in this chapter. We see that the periodicity of this objective-prism selected group of quasars has a slightly larger constant in the logarithm. Another physical group, the three quasars around NGC 3842 shown in the first chapter, fit this larger spacing. In general, each group of quasars we have identified as physically belonging together tends to have either a slightly smaller or slightly larger spacing than the mean of all quasars. This confirms the periodicity, but gives a broadness to the values of preferred redshift for all groups lumped together. Each individual group, however, tends to have more exactly defined peaks of preferred redshift. The final chapter in this book makes some suggestions as to what might cause the fundamental periodicity. What causes the slight difference from group to group? There is only a hint, which will be discussed later in Chapter 9 when we examine Virgo cluster quasars. It is clear that further study and analysis of these periodicities could furnish invaluable insight into these most basic physical properties of matter.

References to Papers Covering Material in Text

1981, Oort, J. H., Arp, H., and de Ruiter, H., Astron. and Astrophys., 95, p. 7.
This paper investigates the properties that quasars would have if they were at cosmological distances and members of superclusters. I thought I might initiate a healthy precedent in the field by looking at the data from a standpoint different from my own personal belief. The paper demonstrates the masterful astronomical knowledge of Prof. Oort and it was a privilege to write the paper with him, but I must admit that the results which I felt to be important about the separations of high-z quasar pairs being too large to be accommodated by the cosmological model were not included in the paper.

1983, Arp, H., "Groups, Concentrations, and Associations of Quasars" in "Quasars and Gravitational Lenses," 24th Liège Astrophysical Colloquium, Institut d'Astrophysique, June 1983.
This review paper developed the data on luminosities of quasars in groups at different distances. The discovery of the line of quasars from M33 first emerged in this presentation. The conference is also interesting to read for the number of papers critical of my general viewpoint about quasars.

1983, Hoyle, F., "A Gravitational Model for QSO's," Preprint Series No. 88, Department of Applied Mathematics and Astronomy, University College, P.O. Box 78, Cardiff, England.

This refreshingly candid discussion of the quasar problem argues for a gravitational mechanism as a cause of the redshift. I do not personally subscribe to this explanation, but the discussion of quasar phenomena is rigorous and informed and the science is top-notch. This monograph is in very few libraries and must be obtained from the University of Cardiff.

1984, Arp, H., "The Nearest Quasars," Publ. Astron. Society of the Pacific, 96, p. 148.

This paper investigates the line of quasars southwest of M33 and shows how low-redshift quasars and radio galaxies are rotated slightly from the line of high-redshift quasars. Of great importance in this paper is the discussion, the most fundamental I could make, of the arguments previously advanced to prove that radio galaxies had to be at their redshift distances.

1984, Arp, H., "A Large Quasar Inhomogeneity on the Sky," Astrophys. Journ. (Letters), 277, p. L27.

This paper offers additional evidence that the quasars southwest of M33 cannot be an accidental fluctuation in a uniform distribution and that this observed distribution makes no sense on the cosmological model. A sad by-note is that George Abell, who was a classmate of mine in my graduate-school days, was refereeing this paper. One of the last letters he wrote before his untimely death said that he could not explain how it occurred, but he was sure the alignment was some sort of selection effect.

1984, Arp, H., "Distribution of Quasars on the Sky," Journ. of Astrophys. and Astronomy, 5, p. 31.

This was an invited paper by V. Radakrishnan for the *Jubilee Issue of the Journal of Astrophysics and Astronomy*. It developed further the picture of the Local Group, quasars with $z \sim 2$ and established consistency between the line of quasars in the Local Group and the next nearest Sculptor group. It showed that inhomogeneities of distribution of the quasars were reflected in inhomogeneous distribution of radio sources. The radio sources have, in the past, been supposed to be uniformly distributed and it is very important now to reinvestigate this important question.

1985, Narlikar. J. V. and Subramanian, "A Statistical Significance of a Large Quasar Inhomogeneity in the Sky," Astron. Astrophys., 151. p. 264.

This shows the concentration of quasars southwest of M33 to be highly significant.

1985, Burbidge, G. R., Narlikar. J. V., and Hewitt, A., Nature, 317, p. 413.

This paper gives the most recent calculation of the chance of accidentally observing the known number of apparent quasar pairs with discordant redshifts. The probability is now less than one in ten thousand, so that the cosmological hypothesis is dropping back badly from an already very bad, earlier position. See the text here and *Nature*, 323, p. 185 for the most recent exchange of viewpoints.

GALAXIES WITH 6 EXCESS REDSHIFT

In the normal course of observing the sky with telescopes, we expect to see galaxies near to each other in groups. When we measure the displacement of the absorption and emission lines in their spectra, we expect to find the redshifts of these galaxies to be very close, differing by only a few hundred kilometers per second (km s⁻¹).

When we do see a much larger redshift, we instinctively feel that it is an unrelated object at a much greater distance in the far background where the expansion velocity of the universe is carrying it away from us more rapidly. It is an enormous shock therefore when we measure two galaxies that are interacting, or connected together, and find that they have vastly different redshifts.

That is what happened when I measured the redshifts of the two galaxies pictured in Figure 6-1. It was 1970 and Palomar observers still had to ride all night in the cage of the 200-inch telescope in order to obtain direct photographs and spectra of astronomical objects. An observer was usually lucky to get two spectra in a night of objects as faint as the ones in Figure 6-1. But I was following up interesting objects from my *Atlas of Peculiar*

Galaxies, and I was interested in that class of objects where companion galaxies were found on the end of spiral arms. As in the case of the quasars, this study led to big trouble when I discovered the redshifts of the two connected objects differed by $\triangle z = 8,300$ km s⁻¹.

The trouble lies in the fact that one cannot even postulate that by some freak accident two galaxies are in the same region of space and that the smaller galaxy is running past the larger galaxy with a relative velocity of 8,300 km s⁻¹. At that rate of passage the companion would be unable to pull out a filament from the larger galaxy. The gravitational pull needed to shear stars out of their normal orbits cannot build up in the relatively short time that such a rapid encounter would allow. We therefore conclude that the objects cannot have this velocity difference and we are back to an object with an intrinsic redshift. Only this time, it is not just a compact object like a quasar, but a whole galaxy of stars, each star of which must share, for some mysterious reason, a redshift much elevated above the normal.

Of course, the first thing one considers in a case like this is whether this could possibly

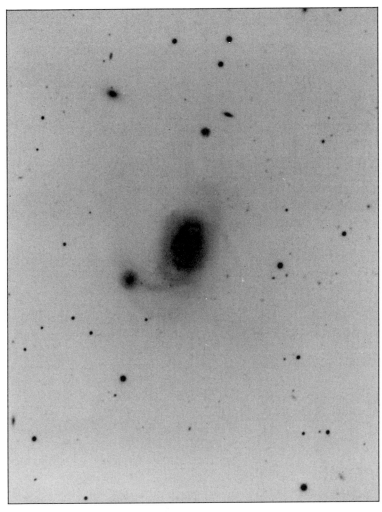

Figure 6-1. The large, disturbed Seyfert galaxy, NGC 7603, with a companion galaxy apparently attached by a filament. The redshift of the larger galaxy is 8,700 km s^{-1} and of the smaller is 17,000 km s^{-1}. These pictures were taken by Roger Lynds with the Kitt Peak National Observatory 4-meter telescope in 1973 and have recently become available through the information adding of separate pictures by Nigel Sharp.

represent a background object that just accidentally happens to appear projected onto the end of a luminous filament belonging to a more nearby galaxy. So back I went into the cage on my next observing run in order to obtain the longest, deepest and best possible photograph of the object. It showed the connection strongly, as did all other pictures like the one shown in Figure 6-1.

Unlike the connection between NGC 4319 and Markarian 205 discussed in Chapter 3, nobody ever tried to question the reality of the luminous arm emerging from NGC 7603. What little debate took place in this case

hinged on whether its connection to the companion was real or only apparent.

A number of arguments attested to a real connection. First of all, the larger galaxy, NGC 7603, is a Seyfert galaxy, a fairly rare kind of galaxy with an active nucleus. Secondly, NGC 7603 is all torn up inside and nothing else is around except the companion to account for this disruption. Thirdly, only one luminous arm or filament emerges from NGC 7603 in such a way as to make it an almost unique object among galaxies. This unusual arm ends right on the companion!

All this, naturally, is extremely unlikely to

be an accidental occurrence. But still I was not satisfied and I studied the companion closely. The original plate showed that the form of the companion, with its broad, bright nucleus and a discretely lower surface brightness disk, is unusual. But the bright rim on the outer edge of the companion, just where the arm from NGC 7603 connects, proved to me that there is actual physical interaction between the two. *

But the spectrum of the companion puzzled me. It had only the usual absorption lines found in ordinary galaxies of older stellar population type. As we will see, a number of other examples of these anomalously redshifted companion galaxies tend instead to show emission lines and absorption lines that are more characteristic of a younger stellar population. The evidence from the nature of the connection and the peculiarities of the galaxies establish rather conclusively that the present two are connected, but the spectrum of the companion so far offers no clues as to unusual physical conditions that might account for its 8,300 km s^{-1} higher redshift.

This was the only example of a strikingly discordant redshift that appeared in this small class of connected companions in the *Atlas of Peculiar Galaxies*. But the much larger *Catalogue of Southern Peculiar Galaxies and Associations*, initiated a few years later by Arp and Madore, furnished more examples of smaller companions connected to, or interacting with, larger galaxies. These were the productive days when I used the 2.5-meter Carnegie Institution telescope in Chile to get further photographs and measure spectra of these objects. In the first batch of seven candidates, I found three to have highly discrepant redshift values. Later more turned up. A sampling of these objects is shown in Figures 6-2 and 6-3 here. The luxury of having long runs on the telescope allowed the spectra of these objects

to be studied in some detail. There are many extraordinary peculiarities discovered in these spectra which should be followed up. But as a preliminary classification I have noted in the sample listed in Table 6-1 whether the spectra have emission lines and whether the absorption lines are characteristic of a young or old stellar population.

We should understand that if we just go around picking galaxies at random in the sky and studying their spectra that by far the most common spectrum we will find is nonemission with late-type stellar absorption. Table 6 shows, however, that the discordant redshift companions characteristically exhibit excited emission lines and young stellar population absorption lines. If they were just accidental projections of ordinary background galaxies they would have the characteristic spectra of background galaxies. This is a clinching proof that these excess redshift companions are really physically associated with the lower redshift galaxies.

The way in which I would think a rational astronomer would have to handle this disturbing situation is to look carefully at objects like NGC 7603 in Figure 6-1, or at some of the examples in Figures 6-2, 6-3, and 6-4, and say: "Well, these are certainly connected objects, the eye readily tells us they could not be anything else." Then, he puts aside the pictures and says, "This goes against everything I have been taught about redshift-distance laws. They must be just accidents." But then he thinks about the confirmatory evidence from their spectra (and the abundant other evidence discussed in this book) that demonstrates they are not accidents. He then goes back to the pictures and says, "Well, it seems that they are not accidents and when I actually *look* at the pictures I can see many more confirmatory details which demonstrate that this is just simply the surprising, but actual

---

*Photographs taken shortly afterward in 1973, with the Kitt Peak National Observatory's 4-meter telescope confirmed the peculiar bright rim on the companion, its deformed shape and the brightening of this rim near its point of contact with the arm from NGC 7603. The existence of these confirming pictures was unknown to me until recently. These latter photographs are shown in Figure 6-1.

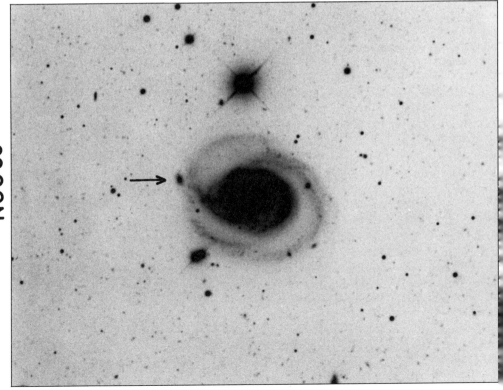

NGC 53

AM 0213-283

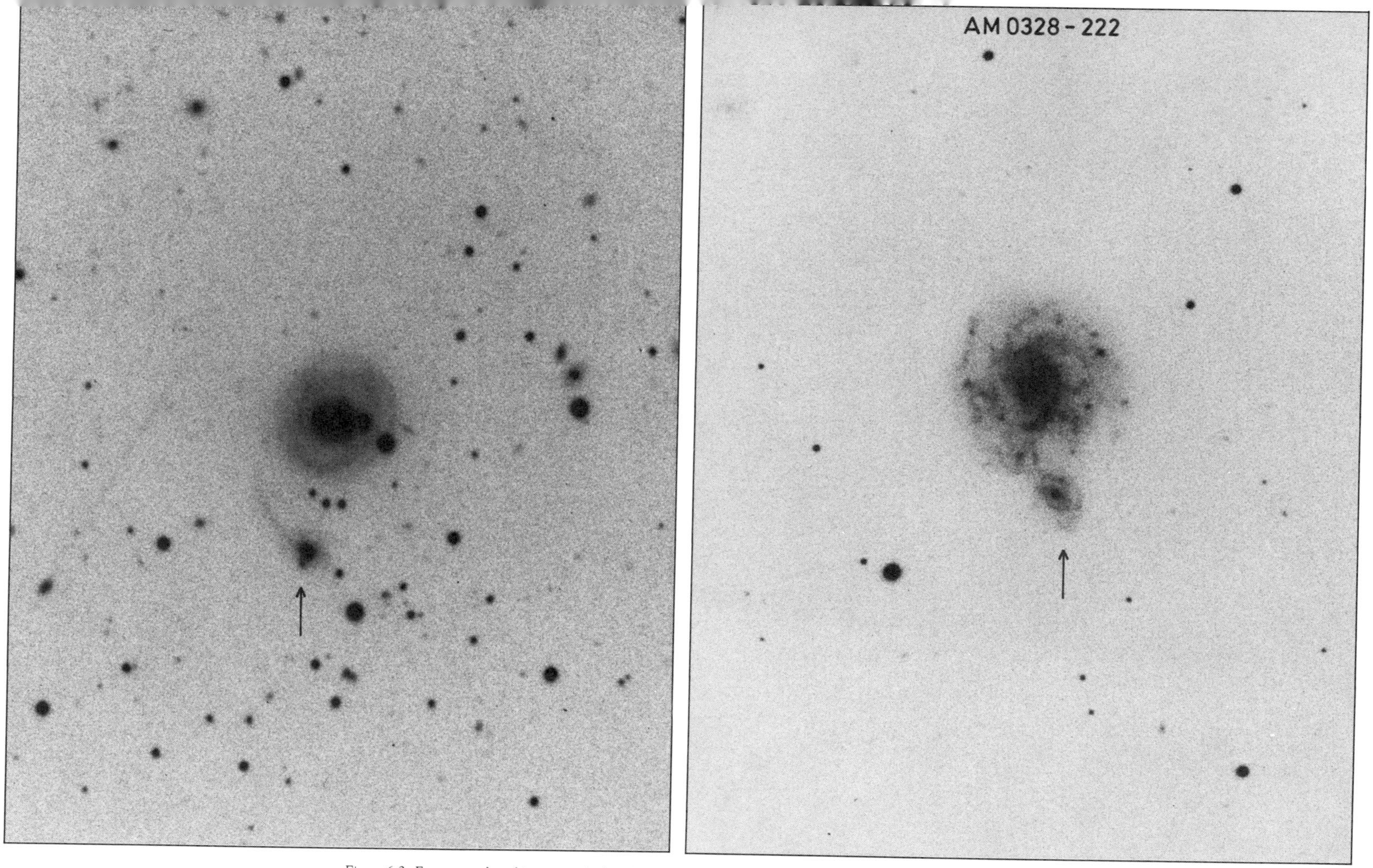

AM 0328 - 222

Figure 6-2. *Four examples of interacting high-redshift companions (marked by arrows). See Table 6-1 for data.*

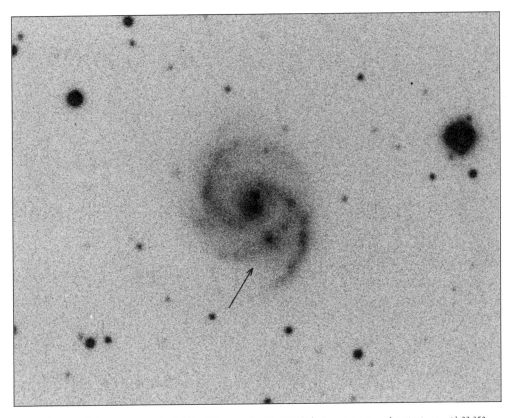

Figure 6-3. A particularly interesting example of a high redshift companion (AM2006-295). Arrow points to condensation in arm with 22,350 km s^{-1} excess redshift.

TABLE 6-1
Sample of Connected or Interacting Galaxies with Large Discordant Redshifts*

Main Galaxy	Companion	Type of Spectrum	Excess Redshift z (km s)	Illustrated in Figure No.
NGC 7603	Comp SE	late absorption	+8,300	6-1
AM0059-402	Comp S	late absorption	+9,695	Arp. J., 239, 471
AM0213-283	Comp N	strong emission early absorption	+9,695	6-2
AM0328-222	Comp S	emission, early absorption	+17,925	6-2
AM2006-295	KN SW	weak emission, peculiar absorption	+22,350	6-3
NGC 1232	Gal B	emission, early absorption	+26,210	6-4
NGC 53	Comp N	emission, early absorption	+32,774	6-2
AM2054-221	Comp E	emission late absorption	+36,460	6-2

*As pictured in Figures 6-2, 6-3, and 6-4. For a more complete listing of cases see *Astrophysical Journal*, 263, p. 70. "Late absorption" described a spectrum typical of low-luminosity, older stars, "Early absorption" is a spectrum typical of high-luminosity, younger stars.

way things are." It is a rare occasion when a person, even a scientist, is able to really look at a picture without forcing it into a frame of prior reference.

It is, in fact, instructive to look more closely at these pictures. For example, in Figure 6-1 one sees two (stellar appearing?) condensations in the filament leading to the companion. This is even stranger behavior for a part of a galaxy to exhibit. What are they? What would spectra with a large telescope and the newest spectrographs reveal about them? Then there is the three-armed spiral galaxy shown in Figure 6-3. Do you realize how rare *three-armed* spirals are? And this third arm originates from a point midway out along one of the two symmetrical arms! The discrepant redshift object occurs in the middle of this third arm. How did it get there?

These questions call for a working hypothesis within which we can try to organize the disparate facts presented by the observations. But we have already described an ejection hypothesis that was needed to explain the origin of quasars in the earlier chapters of this book.

There we saw that the compact objects that were to become quasars, the protoquasars, must emerge from the galaxy's nucleus as relatively small, high-redshift objects and later expand, with their redshifts decaying and the objects becoming more like compact, peculiar companion galaxies. There are several advantages to this hypothesis for the discordant companions described here. (I stress that this is only an empirical hypothesis at this stage— a working scheme to connect the various observations which cannot be explained by the current theories about galaxies.) One advantage is that only one explanation would have to be invented to explain the excess redshifts of both quasars and companion galaxies. If there is a continuous physical evolution between the two, as there appears to be a continuous range of physical properties between them, then the same mechanism for nonvelocity redshifts, in differing amounts, could explain both.

At this point, two comments should be made: (1) The companions with the highest redshifts which are discordant (45,000 km s^{-1} corresponds to a $z = 0.15$) are in the same redshift range as the smaller redshift quasars. (The brightest apparent magnitude quasar in the sky, the famous 3C 273, has $z = 0.16$.) (2) The companions with the highest excess redshifts are spectroscopically the most like quasars. The puzzle I encountered in the spectrum of the companion to NGC 7603 could be resolved if the spectra with relatively small excess redshift are relatively normal, but the spectra become more abnormal as the excess redshift grows. A glance down Table 6-1 shows that with increasing excess redshift, the spectra contain more excited emission lines and younger stellar absorption lines. Quasars are of course characterized by high temperatures and conspicuous emission lines, that is, they are the most extreme of these objects. As for the young stellar absorption spectra, extensive observations of the prototype quasar, 3C 48, enabled the astronomers J.B. Oke and T. Boronson to proudly announce that it had the underlying absorption spectrum of a galaxy—but the absorption spectrum is of the young stellar type!

This last point about underlying galaxies is an interesting and much belabored one. A number of astronomers who have attempted to defend the status quo have tried very hard to prove that underlying all quasars are galaxies. The idea was that there might be some uncertainty about quasars because they are exotic objects, but that galaxies are familiar kinds of objects which must be at their conventional redshift distances. Proving quasars to be galaxies, they felt, was proving quasars to be at their redshift distances (just in case it needed to be proven, which, of course, they claimed was unnecessary). But what has been apparent from the observations all along— even before many of the present investigators started their work—is that quasars and compact, active galaxies are continuous in phyisical properties. So, by proving again that they

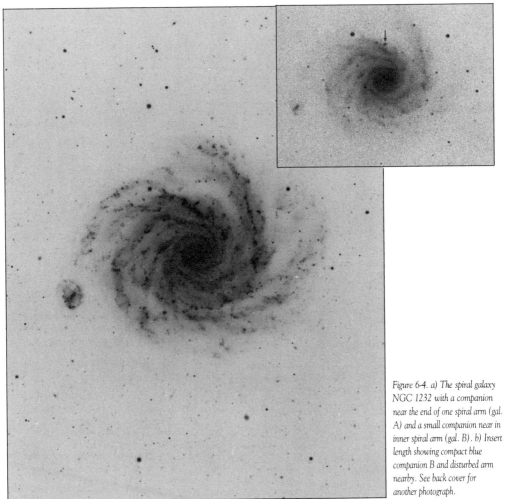

Figure 6-4. a) The spiral galaxy NGC 1232 with a companion near the end of one spiral arm (gal. A) and a small companion near in inner spiral arm (gal. B). b) Insert length showing compact blue companion B and disturbed arm nearby. See back cover for another photograph.

are related kinds of objects they have proven that the evidence for nonvelocity redshifts in quasars is supported by the evidence for nonvelocity redshifts in galaxies—and vice versa.

It is a cruel fact of life that whatever the current, official theory is, it must explain *all* the observed facts. A single well-founded, contradictory observation will suffice to topple the whole edifice. But we have seen that the conventional theory that galaxy redshifts can only be due to Doppler velocity has been violated not just once, but in numerous, independent instances. We will continue to see these violations accumulate.

As of 1982, 38 examples of these discordant redshift companions around 24 main galaxies had been published. We cannot discuss them all here but the references for this data are given in the Appendix. One example is so interesting, however, that I cannot resist devoting a few pages to it.

A. The Large Spiral Galaxy NGC 1232 and its Two Discordant Redshift Companions

As Figure 6-4 shows, NGC 1232 is a large, beautiful spiral. The companion galaxy near the end of the spiral arm shows the same resolution of knots and features as the main galaxy. It is the usual kind of galaxy that large spirals typically have as physical companions. One can even trace the arm which ends near the companion back to the main spiral where it splits, strangely, into a channel about the width of the companion. I would suggest this might be evidence for the companion to have originated within the main spiral and have traveled outward along this arm. Be that as it may, there was never any hesitancy about accepting this galaxy as a run-of-the-mill companion to a large spiral galaxy. Scarce heed was even paid to the fact that the redshifts of both galaxies were cataloged as essentially equal.

But then an unpredictable event occurred. The cataloged redshift for the companion was found to be in error. The redshift of the companion was really 4,776 km s^{-1} greater than the main galaxy. One of the foremost galaxy experts of this era, Gerard de Vaucouleurs, who has been rather more open to discrepant evidence than most, nevertheless had the following comment about this development:

"Until recently I was convinced from appearance and resolution that this was a physical pair, in fact rather similar to our own galaxy and the Large Magellanic Cloud. However, the differential velocity, $\triangle V = +4776$, forces us to conclude that this must be an optical pair unless you can offer compelling proof that the two are physically connected."

My own argument was that the companion was not the kind that was found isolated in space, but was of the kind found with larger spirals such as NGC 1232. Nevertheless, I did take very deep photographic plates of the system in order to search for "compelling proof," perhaps in the form of deformations or extensions of the outer regions of NGC 1232 in the region of the companion. I found no further evidence for the association of the companion than was available originally. But I did find something else that

turned out to be enormously interesting.

Tracing back along the same spiral arm which ends on the companion I noticed an anomalous thickening and deformation, as if something was perturbing the arm at that point. Next to this disturbed part of the arm, I noticed an object. Purely out of curiosity, and fully expecting an H II (gaseous emission) region at the redshift of the main galaxy, I took its spectrum. There was thereupon one of those rare and thrilling moments in research when you can look down a long corridor into the future. The spectrum showed a redshift of over 28,000 km s^{-1} (almost one-tenth the velocity of light!), far exceeding the mere 1,776 km s^{-1} of the main galaxy.

Studying the spectrum was fascinating. There were six separate kinds of peculiarities that indicated the object cannot be any normal kind of background galaxy. Among them the fact of the narrow calcium (K) absorption line implied it was a low luminosity galaxy. But the most compelling argument that the object was at the distance of NGC 1232 was simply that one does not see background galaxies through the disk of a spiral galaxy. The dust and obscuration in the disk of a spiral galaxy, particularly near the arms, simply forms an impenetrable screen. If, by some strange quirk, we were able to see through a thin part of this screen, we would certainly expect a background object to be heavily reddened. But galaxy B, as we call this object, is extremely blue! It is so blue, in fact, that there is no way that it can be any kind of normal galaxy.

This evidence, even though of the most detailed and quantitative kind, has always been simply ignored. One of the purposes of this book is to bring all this evidence together, to show that it massively contradicts the accepted paradigm, and to challenge the establishment to deal in a responsible scientific manner with the observations.

In view of our empirical, working hypothesis we can point out that one way an object like B could arrive at a point in a spiral arm, as observed, is to travel along the spiral arm from the nucleus. It is interesting that this is the same arm along which it was speculated that companion A may have emerged. Perhaps even more suggestive is the knot (KNSW) in the three-armed spiral pictured in Figure 6-3. (That was another of those exciting moments where I took the spectrum expecting a low-redshift emission region.) But that third arm, in my opinion, could only have been formed by an ejection phenomenon along the original track of one of the two main arms. The discordant redshift object then lies along the trajectory of that ejection. There is nothing sacred about this hypothesis, but at least it explains why these discordant redshift objects are found in these arms, an explanation which would be rather difficult otherwise.

The subject of companion galaxies has already been an important topic in this book. We have seen evidence for the origin of high-redshift quasars associated with companions in nearby groups of galaxies. Now we have seen evidence for companion galaxies themselves to be peculiar and to have high nonvelocity redshifts with respect to their main galaxy. The subject of companion galaxies will continue to be an important subject in this book because, as we shall see, the structure of the universe we live in is typically that of groups of galaxies here and there, each dominated by one or two large galaxies with the rest of the galaxies forming a group of smaller companion galaxies around them. It is these smaller, compact objects and companion galaxies in groups which again and again furnish the most abnormal and most excessively redshifted objects that we encounter.

B. The Active Central Galaxy, NGC 4151

In most groups, the central galaxy is not particularly active at the moment. For example, the central galaxy in our own Local Group is M31, a prototypical Sb spiral. (An Sb has a moderate central bulge of stars and not too conspicuous spiral arms.) It contains the majority of mass in the group and is apparently undergoing fairly smooth and regular rotation of its gas, dust, and stars around its center. M81, in the third most distant, major group is an Sb spiral almost identical to M31. Such Sb spirals are typically seen throughout space with their retinue of smaller companions grouped around them. But NGC 4151 is an Sb spiral with a very active nucleus. How active, you may ask! The brilliant point of light in its nucleus is variable, is a source of radio emission and X-rays, and shows broad, high-excitation emission lines. Altogether, the nucleus acts in many ways like a quasar. The person who has studied this nucleus most intensively, and with whom I am well acquainted, has attempted to find clues to the energy sources and energy mechanisms within quasars and active galaxies from large-scale programs of observing and analysis of this nucleus.

But I was always interested in the outer regions of NGC 4151. It is surrounded by a retinue of smaller galaxies. The trouble is that all of these smaller galaxies are of considerably higher redshift. The usual response would be to say that NGC 4151 is accidentally centered on a more distant group of galaxies. Unfortunately for this hypothesis, these smaller galaxies have generally different redshifts between themselves, ruling out their membership in the same group by conventional criteria. As usual, the first step was to get the best possible plate of the field. On a very dark night at Palomar, with exquisite seeing, I obtained the three-hour exposure shown in Figure 6-5. It shows the arm on the north going out and around almost to NGC 4156, the high surface brightness galaxy to the northeast. The other arm of NGC 4151 goes around and out to the south, where it appears to join a smaller galaxy just at the southwest edge of the picture. Since both of these

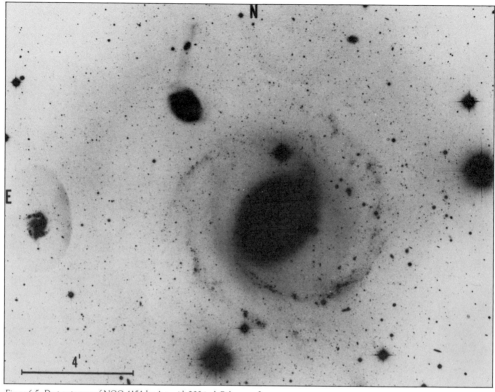

Figure 6-5. Deep exposure of NGC 4151 by Arp with 200-inch Palomar reflector.

smaller galaxies are of considerably higher redshift than NGC 4151 itself, I made a special effort to follow this up.

Eventually, I obtained a number of plates and, with Jean Lorre's help, information-added them to give the high-contrast picture shown in Figure 6-6. I think this picture shows convincingly that a high-redshift galaxy is attached to the end of each NGC 4151 arm. This result seemed so startling that I simply stated it and did not especially emphasize it with respect to the other evidence for the existence of discordant redshifts. But now that further evidence, as discussed earlier in this chapter, shows that objects of excess redshift occur in or along spiral arms, it can be put forward as strong corroborative proof of the phenomenon. It should also be noticed that the values of the redshifts involved are very similar to those in the Stephan's Quintet

system discussed later, in Section E of this chapter.

I have to add a note about B. A. Vorontsov-Velyaminov, a Russian astronomer, who in 1957 searched the Palomar Sky Survey paper prints for peculiar galaxies. One of his favorite kinds was companions on the ends of spiral arms. I learned the English word "gemmation" from him—a botanical term meaning budding or outgrowth. He was always searching for a spiral galaxy with companions on the ends of both arms to demonstrate his theory of galaxy formation. I should dedicate Figure 6-6 to him.

There is a lot more of interest in the NGC 4151 region. It is a very active region in that all sorts of odd objects are found there. The knotty spiral due east of NGC 4151 has H II regions of much larger apparent diameter than those in NGC 4151, even though it is

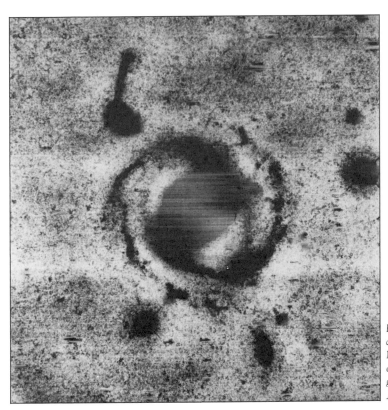

supposed to be five times further away as judged by its redshift. Figure 6-7 shows a small galaxy with a filament leading out of its minor axis to three little emission spots of 22,000 km s⁻¹ higher redshift. Figure 6-8 showns a low surface brightness, dwarfish galaxy of about the same redshift as NGC 4151 attached to a highly peculiar, very high-redshift spiral. (The small spiral is of class Sc I, where "I" means the most luminous, and hence supposedly the most distant kind of spiral galaxy.) If all this evidence seems too much to absorb, it is worth noting that just *one* case like this, any one of these, needs to be established in order to blow the whole conventional viewpoint completely out of the water.

Finally, a straight chain of rather small, high-redshift galaxies extends just to the northwest of the bulge in NGC 4151. This chain serves to introduce the next section of this chapter.

C. Chains and Multiple Interacting Groups In the Vicinity of Large Central Galaxies

During the course of astronomical exploration of the sky, certain very unusual groups of galaxies were noticed. They usually bear names that go far back in the astronomical literature like Stephan's Quintet, Seyfert's Sextet, the Burbidge Chain, and Vorontsov-Velyaminov 150 and 172. Some of these are shown in Figures 6-9, 6-10, and 6-11. Curiously, they seem mostly to be involved with redshift anomalies. That is, some galaxies that appear to belong to these groups have much different redshift. In addition to the redshift anomalies within these groups, the groups also tend to fall close to large, lower redshift galaxies. I decided to investigate this systematically and wrote a brief paper in 1973 pointing out that five out of six of these multiple interacting groups fall remarkably close to

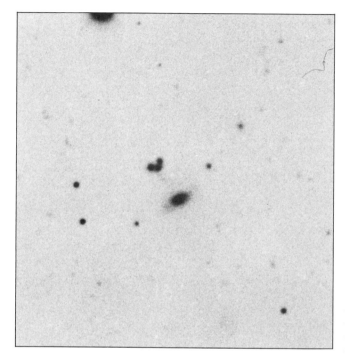

Figure 6-7. Small galaxy northwest of NGC 4151 that has a filament emerging from its minor axis that leads to three compact, emission line objects of much higher redshift.

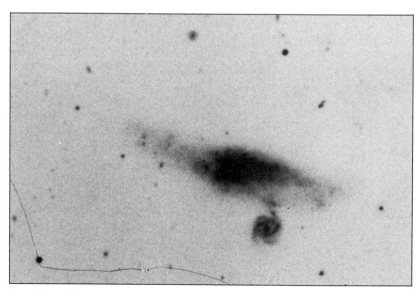

Figure 6-8. Dwarf galaxy north of NGC 4151 with very high redshift spiral attached. This and the preceding four objects from Arp 1977.

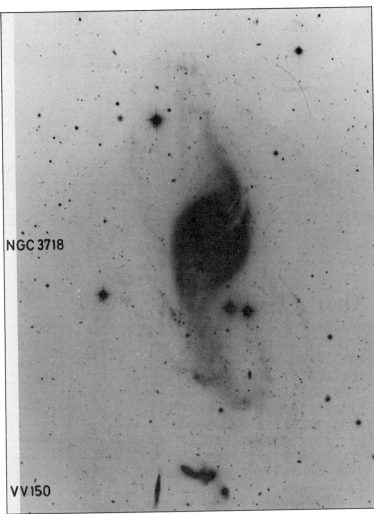

NGC 3718

VV 150

Figure 6-9. *The large barred-spiral galaxy NGC 3718 with arms apparently affected by the interacting chain VV150 which has a +7,000 km s⁻¹ higher redshift. Unpublished measures also indicate low redshift hydrogen coincident with VV150.*

large, low-redshift galaxies. This is not a large number of cases but because interacting systems that are this bright are very conspicuous and very rare, the fact that they fell so close to these large galaxies made for a highly significant proof of association. In order to disprove the association, hundreds of such systems would have had to have been found *not* in the vicinity of large galaxies, a situation that anyone well acquainted with the real sky recognizes as clearly out of the question. It also turned out that these peculiar systems had a distinct tendency to "chain," i.e., fall in a line. A line could not exist for long before peculiar motions of the individual galaxies would disrupt it. So, even from the conventional viewpoint these chains had to be young. All in all, the evidence was quite straightforward that these are young, multiply interacting and aligned systems which often contain anomalous-redshift galaxies and tend to exist as companions to large, low-redshift galaxies. The point was that because these were the brightest and most interactive groups known we could not discover more groups like them. The large proportion of anomalous redshifts were very significant and could never be made to go away. Well, that is what one would think!

But, at this point an analysis came along

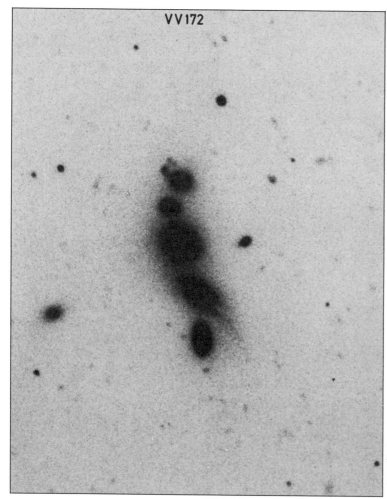

VV 172

Figure 6-10. The famous chain of galaxies VV172; the second from the top has an excess redshift of about 21,000 km s⁻¹.

that to me is the epitome of research which blocks important progress. A student doing a thesis purported to investigate close groups of galaxies over the sky. He reported large numbers of these groups and that statistically there was no evidence for them to contain anomalously redshifted objects. When he came as a postdoctoral fellow to my institution, he gave these results in a colloquium at Caltech. I pointed out that most of his groups were so faint that he could not tell whether they were multiply interacting or not and, even worse, he had not investigated redshifts and had to *assume* there were no deviant redshifts within them. But he and the group

with him brushed aside these points and proclaimed his results as proof that no redshift anomalies existed! Of course, anyone with a minimal knowledge of the field really consciously knew that the galaxies he was dealing with were nothing like the long-famous groups such as Stephan's Quintet and Seyfert's Sextet.

Later, a repeat of this research showed that after plate flaws and other errors had been allowed for, he had overstated the prevalence of these groups by a factor of ten. A factor of ten is rather large. And can you imagine confusing interacting groups like those pictured in Figures 6-9 and 6-10 with plate flaws?

The refutation of this work did not come, however, until six years later and by then the result and the author were well entrenched. Some of the same people who sponsored this researcher were on the telescope time-allocation committee which criticized my research and precipitated the denial of my observing time at Palomar.

D. The Galaxy Chain VV172

Now that we have introduced the subject of galaxy chains, we can show the most famous galaxy chain of all, VV172 (VV is common astronomical shorthand for the Russian astronomer Vorontsov-Velyaminov). In Figure 6-10 we see a close chain of five galaxies, two on either side of a larger central galaxy. Much to the consternation of the astronomer investigating this chain, the second galaxy from the top turned out to have an outstandingly excess redshift. It is startling to run your eye down the list of redshifts from top to bottom and see the anomalous one leap out:

VV 172	
Galaxy A	16,070 km s^{-1}
B	36,880
C	15,820
D	15,690
E	15,480

After mulling this over for a while, the decision was that the anomalous redshift belonged to a background galaxy seen projected accidentally at this precise spot in the chain (what else?). After some time, another astronomer measured the color of galaxy B, actually expecting it to have the normal, reddish color of a distant background galaxy. Instead, it turned out to be abnormally blue. This result, however, was barely mentioned in the literature.

On the evidence from the excess redshift companions in the beginning of this chapter, we would expect the excess redshift object in

VV172 to be bluer, smaller, and more compact than the main galaxy. It is all three. The alignment of companions is something we saw a hint of in Chapters 4 and 5 and will see more of later. The most unusual aspect of VV172 is the relatively large size of the high redshift companion and the relatively large redshift of the remaining galaxies. These facts allowed Jack Sulentic to show how preposterously large the blue companion would be if placed at its redshift distance. But because there has been no further spectroscopic work done on this system since it was discovered to be so strange, it is difficult to form an opinion as to whether it is in fact a distant, highly luminous example of a discordant redshift chain, or whether it is a more nearby object where all members have components of non-velocity redshifts.

E. The Most Famous Multiple Interacting System, Stephan's Quintet

It is perhaps fitting to discuss at this point the brightest and most interactive multiple galaxy system of all (discovered with the Marseille telescope by M. E. Stephan way back in 1877). This system has provoked so many intransigent, partisan papers that I could fully visualize the combatants still stamping their canes on the floor thirty years from now and shouting into each others' hearing aids:

"It isn't!"

"It is!"

Since I cannot possibly give an account of all of this rodomontade, much less a balanced account, I will indulge in the luxury of giving a completely biased account from my own point of view.

The furor started when Geoffrey and Margaret Burbidge took spectra of the Quintet in 1961 and reported that one of the galaxies had a redshift much different from the others. The lower left-hand galaxy in Figure 6-11 has a redshift of only 800 km s^{-1}, whereas the remaining, apparently interacting gal-

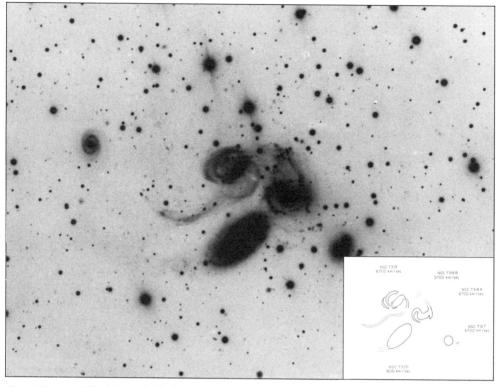

Figure 6-11. a) Deep 200-inch photograph of Stephan's Quintet. Note the low surface brightness tail emerging from NGC 7320. b) Schematic identification of galaxies and redshifts are shown.

axies have redshifts of 5700 and 6700 km s⁻¹. The Burbidges realized immediately that such a difference in redshift has great importance if the galaxies are associated. They pointed out the chance of an accidentally projected interloper was small, about one chance in 1500. It began to look as if this was a singular case, however, when no other groups in which the discordant redshift was the lower redshift were found. But then I realized that it was not the low-redshift object which was anomalous, it was the high-redshift objects. The low-redshift object, NGC 7320, is a fairly normal dwarf galaxy of approximately the same redshift as the neighboring large Sb spiral, NGC 7331 (see Fig. 6-12). It is the multiply interacting, high-redshift galaxies which are anomalous if at the same distance as the low-redshift Sb and its dwarf companion. This is where the previous research on such multiply interacting systems became so important. This is because it had shown that such nonequilibrium systems typically fell in the neighborhood of large, nearby galaxies. (The association of nonequilibrium companions with large galaxies was later confirmed again by a larger survey of all large, nearby spiral galaxies brighter than apparent magnitude 12.0, which was carried out by J. W. Sulentic, H. Arp, and G. di Tullio.)

So the implication was that the reasonably normal, low-redshift dwarf, NGC 7320 and also the peculiar, high-redshift galaxies were all physical companions to NGC 7331. It was just that in this particular case, they happened to all fall very close to each other in space. But if fate were kind enough to give some proof of this hypothesis, then Stephan's Quintet would be a very important system indeed!

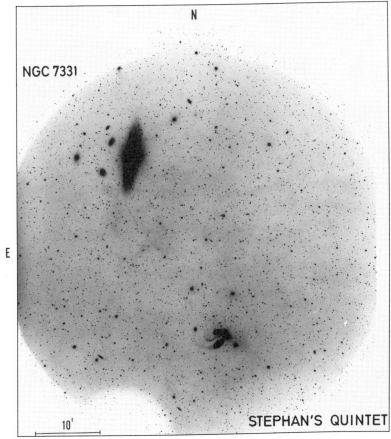

NGC 7331

N

E

10'

STEPHAN'S QUINTET

Figure 6-12. Deep photograph of a larger area around Stephan's Quintet (which is in lower right) with KPNO 4-meter reflector. The picture shows high-redshift companions just east along the minor axis of NGC 7331 and similar high-redshift members of Stephan's Quintet around the low redshift NGC 7320.

The first strong support for the physical association of all the members came from the observation of radio-emitting material which appeared to connect NGC 7331 to Stephan's Quintet. This radio material, as recorded with the resolution available in 1966, is shown by the isophotes in Figure 6-13. At that time, I had never done any astronomy other than optical, but I asked whether I might use the 64-meter radio antenna at Goldstone, the antenna that the Jet Propulsion Laboratory used to communicate with NASA satellites, to look at this region around NGC 7331/Stephan's Quintet. I found a nest of radio sources! They are indicated by the plus symbols in Figure 6-13. These results were published in 1972 and drew the attention of Martin Ryle's radio establishment in England. Observation with

their large interferometer confirmed this excess of bright radio sources. It was concluded, however, that they were a background group of radio galaxies. (This was somewhat strange since this laboratory has consistently claimed that radio sources are not clustered.)

Later, M. Kaftan-Kassim and J. W. Sulentic made further radio measures with the National Radio Astronomy telescope at Green Bank and reported a diffuse bridge of radio-emitting material between NGC 7331 and Stephan's Quintet. Then, a group using the 100-meter antenna at Effelsburg disputed the existence of this bridge, and no further measurements were made. It is instructive to reflect on this sequence of events. The original, crude measurements revealed the existence of radio emission between NGC 7331 and Stephan's Quintet. Later, measurements with

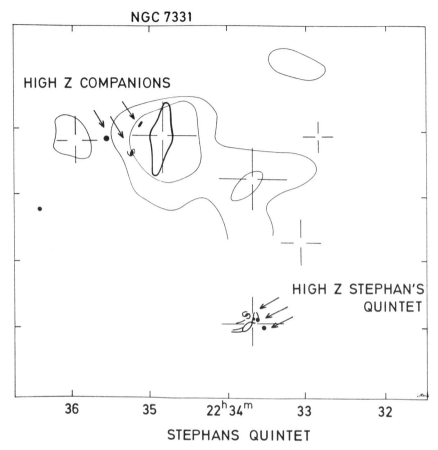

Figure 6-13. Isophotes show the earliest radio measures in the region, plus-marks show the excess of strong radio sources later discovered in this region using the JPL antenna. Open symbols represent low redshift (800 km s⁻¹); filled symbols bright, high redshift (5700 to 6900 km s⁻¹) galaxies.

more powerful telescopes confirmed this. But emphasis was put on the fact that *fainter* radio sources in the region were distributed normally and the question was strongly argued whether the radio material was diffuse or in the form of compact sources. What of course was lost was the strength of the whole evidence, taken together, for the physical association the objects. We see many examples in this book of association of galaxies, radio sources, and discordant redshift objects. What happened in the present case was typical in that more detailed observations with new and advanced instruments were selectively interpreted with old assumptions; the net result was loss of perspective and an ac-

tual retrogression in scientific knowledge.

Also ignored was the extension of radio emission to the east of the dominant Sb. NGC 7331, which encompasses the bright companions of 6300, 6400, and 6900 km s⁻¹ redshift (see Figures 6-12 and 6-13). Of course, just the grouping on the sky of these high-redshift objects, on the one hand, around the low-redshift NGC 7331 and, on the other hand, around the low-redshift NGC 7320 demonstrates their physical association. This phenomenon is typical of large central galaxies (see for egs., NGC 4448 and NGC 1808 mentioned in the appendix).

But strong evidence for the association of high and low redshift objects also came from the apparent interaction within Stephan's Quintet itself. The first attempt to argue against this latter, very obvious conclusion came by a good friend of mine, who became a distinguished galaxy researcher and cosmologist. Gustav Tammann pointed out that the emission (H II) regions in the low-redshift NGC 7320 were large and well-resolved, and that this placed the galaxy at the same distance as NGC 7331. But the low-redshift member was only an anomaly when the Quintet was first discovered. Now he was simply confirming the conclusion that the low-redshift member was a close companion of NGC 7331. Amusingly, he failed to comment on the fact that the H II regions in the 5700 km s^{-1} member were as large in apparent size, indicating an essentially equivalent distance for this high-redshift galaxy.

Thus the battle evolved into trying to prove that the high-redshift members were really at their redshift distance; that is eight times farther away than that of the low-redshift members. The first stab at this came about the time of the IAU symposium in Australia in 1973 (see Appendix to Chapter 2). It was reported that radio measurement of neutral hydrogen contained in the high-redshift galaxies was about normal for galaxies at their redshift distance, purportedly proving that they were at that distance. This "irrefutable" proof lasted only a few years after which it was discovered that the hydrogen wasn't in the galaxies at all—but lay in a distorted position between them, now presumed to be caused by some sort of collision among the high-redshift members. This result was then once again interpreted as a demonstration that the high-redshift members of the Quintet lay in the far, unrelated background. What it actually was, was another proof that these high-redshift galaxies are an extraordinary set of objects and that interpreting them as normal background objects is extremely unwise.

At this point, it seems best to summarize the points as they stand today, in my judge-

ment, both for and against the high-redshift objects being in the background. The points in favor of the large distance are:

(1) In 1971, the Director of the Observatory at Padova, L. Rosino, discovered a supernova in the high-redshift member, NGC 7319. Supernovae are classical indicators of distance, particularly large distances, because these exploding stars are supposed to become as luminous as the whole galaxy in which they appear. At the distance of NGC 7331/7320, one would normally have expected a supernova to be as bright as the large Sb galaxy, NGC 7331, not the much fainter apparent magnitude it was observed to attain. This is a strong point in favor of the large distance of the high-redshift members. But I must say the contrary evidence is even stronger, in my opinion, and I must conclude that the stars in the anomalously redshifted systems simply do not get as bright as in galaxies of lower intrinsic redshift. There is dramatic, but so far ignored, support for this conclusion in that the slightly excess redshift (but highest excess in their groups) companions like M82 and NGC 404 (see chapters 7 and 8) have strikingly less luminous stars than other companion galaxies in the same groups. Also, it seems to me that if one thinks about the recent claim by P. Biermann and others that M82 has many supernovae, these supernovae also must be considerably underluminous.

(2) The width of the absorption lines in the spectra of the high-redshift members was measured. This width, which turned out to be large, was interpreted as due to the dispersion in the velocities of the stars in the systems. This in turn implied a large mass, which in turn implied a high intrinsic luminosity for the systems, and thus required a large distance to the systems because they appear relatively faint in apparent magnitude. This point I also take seriously. But again it is outweighed for me by the evidence that these objects are nearby. I must conclude that being nearby objects, they are extremely peculiar,

and that to take their absorption line widths as luminosity indicators assumes the unlikely circumstance that they would behave as normal galaxies. Their spectra should be studied much more intensively.

The points against large distances are:

(1) Sb spirals such as NGC 7331 typically have high-redshift companions associated with them.

(2) Groups of multiple interacting galaxies appear significantly close to large spirals and typically include excess-redshift members. The high-redshift members of Stephan's Quintet are quintessential examples of this kind of grouping.

(3) Radio connections or associated radio sources appear between NGC 7331, Stephan's Quintet, and galaxies of similar high redshift immediately to the east of NGC 7331.

(4) Very faint surface brightness features revealed by image processing of the deepest wide-field exposures (Arp and Lorre) indicate luminous filaments reaching from Stephan's Quintet back toward NGC 7331.

(5) The deepest 200-inch plates that I have been able to obtain clearly show a "tail" coming out of the southeast end of NGC 7320.

(Actually, an amateur astronomer named Brownlee, in the dark skies of Colorado, photographed this tail very well with a small telescope—it is amazing that so many professionals have such difficulty seeing it.) The shape, orientation, and resolution of the tail all suggest strongly that it belongs to the low-redshift member. A tail like this from NGC 7320 would be decisive. If it really originates from NGC 7320, as all present observations indicate, it must be an interaction tail—which could arise only from physical interaction with the adjacent high-redshift members of the Quintet. That would prove the high-redshift members to be at the close distance. (Actually, measures by Sulentic and Arp with the 1000-foot Arecibo radio dish indicate

that there is low-redshift hydrogen displaced from NGC 7320. Moreover, it was shown that NGC 7320 is peculiarly hydrogen-deficient, as if its interstellar hydrogen had been removed in a collision with another galaxy. There is a strong case for the interaction of NGC 7320 with the high redshift members of the Quintet. It is amazing, or perhaps significant, that the astronomers with access to large radio telescopes keep on measuring the high-redshift hydrogen in the system and keep on avoiding measurement of the low-redshift hydrogen.)

(6) But curiously enough, the most conclusive proof for me that the system is an interaction of high-redshift system with low, is a fact that has been known from the start, from the Burbidges' original 1961 redshift measurements. This fact is that NGC 7318 A and B, those two galaxies in the middle that are so mashed together that they look like one deformed object, actually have redshifts that differ by 1000 km s⁻¹.

There is first of all the question of how could the orderly expansion of the Universe include such deviant, aberrant velocities. (In technical jargon, the Hubble flow is supposed to be at least "quieter"—contain velocities which deviate by less—than 100 km s⁻¹ as we shall discuss later.) But most extraordinary of all, how could this one peculiar velocity, maverick object, with all the universe to choose from, score such an exact hit on one of the members of this group? For this reason I do not believe these two obviously interacting galaxies have an actual velocity difference of 1000 km s⁻¹. In any case, the conventional viewpoint must somehow tell us why it is so easy to accept a 1000 km s⁻¹ redshift discrepancy between interacting systems and so difficult to accept a 5000 km s⁻¹ discrepancy.

Another telling piece of evidence for interaction with the lowest-redshift galaxy in the group is that both X-ray maps and continuum radio maps show strong radiation coming from just the junction region between this

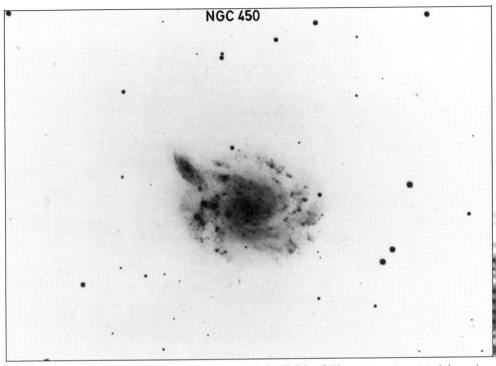

Figure 6-14. Spiral galaxy NGC 450, with apparent companion near its NE edge. "Pathologically" large emission regions exist in the larger galaxy near apparent point of contact.

melded pair, NGC 7318 A and B, and the low-redshift NGC 7320. If these systems are actually contiguous in space then this radiation arises exactly from where the matter in the low-redshift system meets the matter from the high-redshift system. This radiation would then be telling us something about the interaction of the matter in the intrinsically high-redshift system with more normal matter. This would be one of the few experiments given to us to measure the actual physical properties of the new phenomenon. It would seem that the burden of proof falls on the people who believe the two redshift systems to be physically unrelated to tell us why, in this case, radio and X-ray emission would be coming from just the region of apparent interaction.

To sum up the discussion, if one accepts the abundant evidence of the association of high-redshift, peculiar galaxies with nearby galaxies, then Stephan's Quintet is just a par-

ticularly nearby example and just another one of a number of proofs of these associations.

Closer study of the system would allow us to study the actual physical nature of the phenomenon producing the nonvelocity redshifts. For those that insist redshifts can only be caused by velocity, however, the system must be an enormous stack of coincidences piled one on top of another. Moreover, all the other examples of similar systems must, in every single case, also be chance coincidences.

F. NGC 450

To close this chapter I would like to present what to me is a genuine enigma, a case where I am still undecided. It is an object pointed out to me by William Tifft as a possible example of a galaxy with a high-redshift companion. It is shown here in Figure 6-14. I was impressed when I first looked at it on

Schmidt sky survey prints because the main galaxy has three huge gaseous emission regions at just the apparent point of interaction with the small companion. The smaller galaxy to the northeast (NE) has a redshift of $z = 11,600$ km s^{-1} but the main galaxy has a redshift of only $z = 1,900$ km s^{-1}. The emission knots in the main galaxy were so unprecedented that an expert in H II regions who had previously studied the galaxy had simply assumed they were foreground stars.

Two astronomers recently measured the rotation curves (redshift versus apparent distance from the center of the galaxy) of both the main galaxy and the companion. They reported the result in a paper entitled, "The Noninteracting Spiral Pair NGC 450/UGC 807." Probably I was the only person to read past the conclusion stated in their title. But there in the actual data I found some very impressive evidence for interaction. Let us first give the evidence for noninteraction:

(1) The smaller-appearing galaxy has sufficient change in redshift along its major axis to normally indicate that it has fast rotation and therefore high mass and is therefore a large galaxy far behind the main galaxy.

(2) Morphologically, it looks rather like a type of galaxy we would ordinarily regard as luminous and therefore distant.

On the side favoring interaction is:

(1) The end of the smaller galaxy which is toward NGC 450 is somewhat extended and deformed. What is extended is actually the underlying spiral pattern of the small galaxy and is not an effect due to overlying material from the larger one.

(2) The enormous H II regions are extremely unusual and occur almost at the point of apparent contact between the large and the small galaxy.

(3) The rotation curve of the small galaxy is asymmetrical and has a large "dip" on the SW side just as it passes closest to the large galaxy. The overall rotation curve is not, in its shape, like either a large or small galaxy but instead like a curious mixture of the two types.

Finally, the main galaxy itself has a conspicuous discontinuity in its rotation curve just about at the radius of the giant H II regions which is also the radius at which apparent contact with the companion galaxy occurs. All of these last points imply interaction but were excused as being perfectly "normal" for galaxies. But then I wondered what would be taken as evidence for "abnormal." As I said at the outset, I am still undecided about this system and would look hard at it with high-resolution H I maps in order to get more information.

But I was rather deeply impressed by an occurrence at an astronomical conference in 1983. During a break, I noticed across the room a knot of astronomers standing around conducting the real business of astronomy. The senior author of "Noninteractions" was overheard to say, "Well, I asked Chip to give me his best example of discrepant redshifts, and when I measured it there was no evidence at all of interaction."

Of course, I was the one who had urged this astronomer to measure the object; it was certainly not the best example, and quite a bit of evidence had been uncovered—or perhaps I should say covered—in the observation. With all the rest of the statement I agreed except it was said with remarkably more fervor than the occasion seemed to require.

The possibility of quasars in the vicinity of NGC 450 are discussed by Swings et al. on page 37 of the 1983 Liege Symposium (see the Appendix to Chapter 5).

Of course, most astronomers believe they know all about rotation curves of galaxies. They believe that the velocity of material in orbit is determined by the mass of the galaxy inside that orbit. But a surprising situation is then encountered: The velocity of rotation stays just about constant no matter how far from the center of a rotating galaxy one observes. In order to explain this they have to invent unseen, or dark matter. But it has always to appear, miraculously, at just the right radius and in just the right amount.

Hypotheses include everything from subatomic particles like neutrinos to dark rocks surrounding galaxies, so that as one observes outer, fainter regions, the mass continues to rise. But in actuality, postulating undetected matter is equivalent to inventing observations which do not exist in order to explain contradictions to our currently assumed physical laws.

Nobody has detected the hypothetical "missing mass." A few venturesome intellects like J. Bekenstein, M. Milgrom, and R. Sanders have considered that instead the gravitational force law that we assume for the nearby planetary system (general relativity) may be different on the very large scale of galaxies. Unlike the conventional theories,

theirs could be contradicted by observations, but so far has not been. Such considerations, if true, might have considerable consequences for rotation curves of objects like the apparent companion NE of NGC 450 which we just discussed. This would be particularly worth considering if the companion is at the distance of NGC 450, with an intrinsic redshift and therefore physically very peculiar.

When astronomers are trained in graduate schools, one of the few laws that can be taught with any rigor and generality is the law of gravity. This offers one of the few opportunities to make a model of a galaxy. Most astronomers enter research anxious to scale the ladder of success by applying what they have learned to the world of observations. But perhaps we should remember the unknown sage who remarked: "To a man with a hammer in his hand, everything looks like a nail."

Appendix to Chapter 6

Starting with the publication of the first example shown in Figure 6-1 (NGC 7603) the following papers include photographs and details of the systems which contain galaxies with discordant redshifts:

1971, Arp, H., Astrophys. Letters, 7, p. 221.
1980, Arp, H., Astrophysical Journal, 239, p. 469.
1982a, Arp, H., Astrophysical Journal, 256, p. 54.
1982b, Arp, H., Astrophysical Journal. 263, p. 54.

The most recent tabulation of objects appears in the last reference, p. 70. The last reference also contains the color photograph of the spiral NGC 1232 and its companions.

The analysis of the neighborhood of the famous Seyfert galaxy, NGC 4151, including photographs of many key, discordant redshift galaxies is given in:

1977, Arp, H., Astrophysical Journal, 218, p. 70.

The paper which initially discussed bright, multiply interacting galaxies is:

1973, Arp, H., Astrophysical Journal, 185, p. 797

The paper which claimed these discordant redshifts were not unlikely is:

1977, Rose, J., Astrophysical Journal, 211, p. 311.

The subsequent paper showing the density of these systems had been overestimated by a factor of 10 is:

1983, Sulentic, J. W., Astrophysical Journal, 270, p. 417.

Meanwhile, a major project, a survey of 99 bright spiral galaxies carefully compared to distant, control fields without such galaxies had shown that interacting companion systems are significantly associated with the central, bright spirals. This paper is:

1978, Sulentic. J. W., Arp, H., and di Tullio. G. A., Astrophysical Journal, 220, p. 47.

The latest discussion of VV172, the famous chain of galaxies with the very discordant member, is contained in a discussion of image processing techniques:

1983, Sulentic, J. W., Astronomy and Astrophysics, 120, p. 36.

A good nontechnical exposition of image processing techniques applied principally to multiply interacting systems is:
1984, Sulentic, J.W., and Lorre, J., Sky and Telescope, May, p. 407.

There are many papers on Stephan's Quintet. Some references providing the best photographic material are:
1972, Arp, H., and Kormendy, J., Astrophysical Journal Letters, 178, p. L101.
1973, Arp, H., and Kormendy, J., Astrophysical Journal, 183, p. 411.
1976, Arp, H., and Lorre, J., Astrophysical Journal, 210, p. 58.

The latest references to published papers on Stephan's Quintet may be obtained from:
1982, Sulentic, J. W., and Arp, H., Astronomical Journal, 88, p. 267.

Many examples exist of large, low-redshift galaxies surrounded by a retinue of companions of variously higher red-shift. One is NGC 4448 (first of the following references) and another is NGC 1808 (second reference).
1983, Wakamatsu, K., and Arp, H., Astrophysical Journal, 273, p. 167. (Plate 14 and Table 2).
1984, Schnurr, G., University of Bochum, West Germany (submitted for publication).

The paper which discusses the "Noninteracting Spiral Pair NGC 450/UGC 807" is:
1983, Rubin, V.C., and Ford, W.K., Astrophysical Journal, 271, p. 556.

Readers should consult this article, and weigh the claim of undisturbed rotation curves against the actual evidence shown in Figures 2, 3, and 4 of that paper.
1984, Sanders, R.H., European Southern Observatory Scientific Preprint No. 439.

This paper discusses an alternative to "missing mass" for the explanation of the strange behavior of galaxy rotation curves.

SMALL EXCESS REDSHIFTS, THE LOCAL GROUP OF GALAXIES, AND QUANTIZATION OF REDSHIFTS 7

The discovery of the association with normal galaxies of peculiar, high-redshift companions made it clear that most of the excess redshifts of these smaller galaxies must be of nonvelocity origin. In contemplating the staggering problem this raises, it occurred to me that the magnitude of these excess redshifts might extend down to rather small amounts. On a macroscopic scale nature should not be discontinuous. Where would we look for examples of these smaller excess redshifts? The obvious answer is: in the well-known companions of large, nearby galaxies. Therefore, in 1970, I looked at the redshifts of the long-accepted physical companions of the nearest large galaxies like M31 and M81. The companion redshifts were systematically greater! I remember feeling a sense of wonder that this obvious effect had gone unnoticed, and a little awe that the high excess redshift phenomenon had been supported in such an unexpected and unequivocal way by these systematic small excess redshifts.

The reason that this systematic redshift could not arise from a velocity (Doppler effect) is that these companions had long been accepted by all astronomers as belonging to the dominant galaxies. In that case they should be in orbit around these central galaxies and we should see on the average as many coming towards us (relative blueshifts) as going away from us (relative redshifts). If their mean *velocities* were away from us then these companions would be drifting away from the central galaxy and always just in the direction we happened to be looking. This is a *reductio ad absurdum* and proves that the mean redshift of these companions must be due to something other than velocity. Whatever the intrinsic redshift effect which operates in the high excess redshift companions, this same effect is apparently shared, to some extent at least, by all companions.

This effect needed to be validated by other astronomers, of course. Predictably, not all shared my enthusiasm. I first pointed out the effect among 16 well-established companions in 1970. Soon a young astronomer put forward the case of the Sculptor Group of Galaxies, which he claimed violated the relation. There was an ambiguity, however, as to which large galaxies were actually in his Sculptor

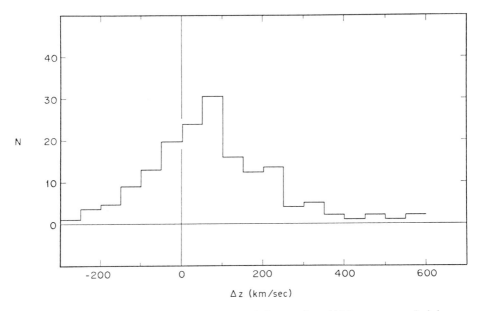

Figure 7-1. *The distribution of companion galaxy redshifts with respect to the dominant galaxy redshift* ($\Delta z = z_{comp} - z_{main}$, *for the largest, most accurate, and recent sample of galaxy groups.*

group and which were dominant. But the one fact which was not ambiguous was that all the fainter members of the group were considerably redshifted. This was ignored in the presentation. Next came a serious and responsible investigation of the effect by two French astronomers, Lucette Bottinelli and Lucienne Gougenheim. In 1973, they measured the wavelength of the line radiation emitted by neutral hydrogen of galaxies in groups. This technique provided very accurate redshifts of companion galaxies in nearby groups and showed that 31 out of 52, or 71%, of the companions had excess redshifts. Their average redshift with respect to the largest galaxies in the group was +90 km s⁻¹.

This result was promptly criticized by a theoretician who said that the effect was not present in their observations but that in any case it was explained by the radial expansion of companions away from their central galaxies. We will discuss the expansion model in a moment, but the statement that the effect was not observationally present was soon contradicted by yet another study. In this study,

the French astronomers Suzy Collin-Souffrin and Jean-Claude Pecker, and the Armenian astronomer H. M. Tovamssian showed that 24 out of a sample of 29 new companions were positively redshifted. Those companions that were compact (high surface brightness) were redshifted the most, an average of +121 km s⁻¹. In 1976, at the Paris Conference, I viewed this evidence and reported that in the two nearest major groups of galaxies, M31 and M81, that 12 out of 12 certain and 18 out of 20 probable group members had positive redshifts which averaged +120 km s⁻¹ with respect to the central galaxy. These investigations were then followed, down through the years, by the investigations listed in Table 7-1. Every one of these investigations has found the companion galaxies systematically redshifted with respect to the dominant galaxy in the group!

The results of the most recent investigation are shown in Figure 7-1. The histogram summarizes the measures on over 260 galaxies from more than 80 different groups. All these galaxies have been observed with radio tele-

TABLE 7-1
Summary of Separate Analyses of Companion Redshifts

Galaxy Groups	Ratio of + Δz's	Average Δz km s⁻¹	Reference
M31, M81, and interacting companions	16/19 = 0.84	+72	Arp 1970
Nearby groups	37/52 = 0.71	+90	Bottinelli and Gougenheim 1973
Byurakan classifications	24/29 = 0.83	+121 (compact) +46 (less compact)	Collin-Souffrin, Pecker and Tovmassian 1974
M31, M81 Certain	12/12 = 1.00	+121	Arp 1976
M31, M81 Probable	18/20 = 0.90	+123	Arp 1976
Southern Hemisphere companions	36/51 = 0.71	+122 ±34	Arp 1982
H I companions	16/23 = 0.70	+63 ±19	Arp 1982
Karachentsev spiral companions of E's	56/94 = 0.60	+100	Giraud, Moles, and Vigier 1982; Sulentic 1982
Karachentsev spiral	39/53 = 0.74	+49	Arp, Giraud, Sulentic, and Vigier 1983
H I groups (Δz ≤ 600 kms⁻¹)	108/159 = 0.68	+64	Arp and Sulentic 1985 Astrophys. J., 291
M31 and M81	21/21 = 1.00	+119 ±13	Arp and Sulentic 1985 Astrophys. J., 291
Spiral dominant groups from Huchra & Geller (1983)	33/51 = 0.65	+30.5 significant at P = .999 level	Sulentic 1984, Astrophys. J., 286, 441

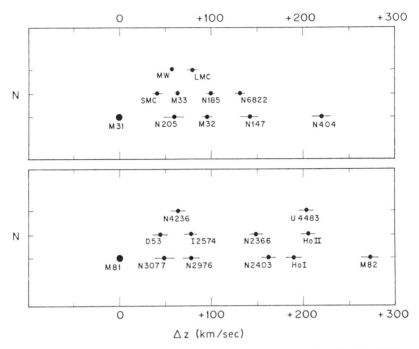

Figure 7-2. Distribution of the relative redshifts of all major companions with respect to the dominant galaxy in the M31 and M81 groups.

scopes which measure the frequency of their neutral hydrogen emission and consequently give extremely accurate redshifts—for the most part more accurate than ±8 km s⁻¹. The predominance of redshifts over blueshifts in this study is unequivocal, as seen in Figure 7-1.

Yet, one referee insisted that we compute the "statistical significance" of the redshift excess. Another refused publication of the paper on the excuse that he was not sure about the membership in the groups. Groups in our study were simply defined as galaxies that fell conspicuously close to each other on the sky and had closely the same redshift—by conventional standards just the definition of groups which has been traditionally accepted as defining the typical structures which inhabit extragalactic space. A variation of this objection, again the only possible avenue of escape, is that the excess numbers of higher redshift companions are due to contamination of the groups by background galaxies.

But this hypothesis can now be unequivocally rejected because the excess of positive redshifts holds strongly as Δz approaches zero. That is the point where dominant galaxies and companions are at exactly the same distance by traditional redshift criteria so there can be no background!

The most devastating result of all, however, is encountered if we examine two of the nearest, best known groups to us, the M31 (Local Group) and M81 groups. There all the companions, which have been accepted for generations as physical members of these two groups, are systematically redshifted with respect to the dominant galaxy. Their redshifts are now all so accurately known that they could never be appreciably changed. Figure 7-2 shows that 21 out of 21 of the major companions in these groups are positively redshifted. This has only one chance out of *two million* of happening accidentally if the companions were to have equal numbers of plus and minus orbital velocities.

Even if one adds smaller and less certain companions to the Local Group, as considered by Yahil, Sandage, and Tammann in their study, one still finds 22 out of 25 positive redshifts in the Local Group alone. Moreover, the discovery of smaller systems in the future cannot alter the fact that the overwhelming mass of material comprising companion galaxies as pictured in Figure 7-2 has a significantly positive redshift. In my opinion, Figure 7-2 represents definitive proof of a nonvelocity redshift phenomenon which must be accepted as it stands. One cannot use the excuse that we have to "study" the situation for an unlimitedly longer time. We know we are not going to discovery any more major blueshifted companions in the closest groups to us, M31 and M81. One cannot postpone or duck the problem. One is forced to deal with the situation as it is now. Since one cannot change any of the Δz's, there is no way to get an equal number of negatives and positives as demanded by conventional theory.

During the one and a half years that the *Astrophysical Journal* was holding up the paper on the observational results, other astronomers were working to explain them. One paper explaining the results was actually written and accepted for publication while the editor was still refusing to publish the paper which outlined the actual problem as just discussed. This explanatory paper which was accepted so quickly, however, revived the old expanding companions model, and I will comment on it here.

The idea is that if all the companions are expanding away from the central galaxy, and if the group subtends an appreciable angle on the sky as we see it, then we will observe a larger volume in back of the central galaxy—receding velocities—than we see in front of the central galaxy—approaching velocities. This can be most easily visualized by saying we would partially see the effect of being inside an expanding group where we would see receding velocities in every direction we looked.

I was in favor of publishing this model (subsequent to the original observational paper, of course) because (1) the authors believed the model and wished to publish it, (2) it refuted the criticism that background contamination is responsible for the effect, and (3) if astronomers feel there is some possibility of having even a semi-respectable explanation they will be more disposed to pay attention to the observations.

But the consequences of this explanation are quite startling, as will be quickly realized. If the companions had been expanding away from the central galaxy at the hypothesized rate since the date of the usually accepted birth of galaxies (some 20 billion years ago), they would have cleared out a shell roughly 2-3 megaparsecs in radius. But the radius of the whole Local Group is only about 1 megaparsec! One would be forced to embrace a model of continuous creation and expulsion of companion galaxies. There may be some truth to this model, as implied by our previous suggestion of ejection of quasars and compact objects which evolve into companion galaxies. But unless the ejection was very slow or subsequently arrested, it would violate the size we find for groups. You can imagine, also, how badly this expanding model would sit with conventional theorists who believe all galaxies condensed at more or less the same time out of clouds in the intergalactic medium. But most telling of all, this model would not cure the intrinsic redshift problem. That is because as we look toward the center of our Local Group, close to the center, we see companions that belong to M31. See, for example, Figure 8-11 at the end of the next chapter. These companions are essentially all redshifted with respect to M31. If a large component of their positive redshift were not intrinsic then we should see some number of them with approaching blueshifts on the pure expansion model. We essentially see none. The same is true of the companions physically close to M81 and also in the remaining groups at greater distances. Moreover, we should expect a redshift (recession) between our galaxy and M31. Instead we see a blueshift. This is a key point in favor of intrinsic shifts as we shall see in the following chapter. But first we are about to encounter another shocking observational result that requires a large part of these redshifts to be nonvelocity.

A. The Quantization of Redshifts

In 1976, William Tifft of the Steward Observatory, reported a long, careful series of measurements of binary galaxies. These are galaxies so close together and of such similar redshift that they are accepted as being physically associated, presumably orbiting around each other. The startling part of his report, however, was that the differences in redshift between members of these pairs of galaxies were quantized in steps of 72 km s⁻¹ (principally $\triangle z$ = 72, 144, and 216 km s⁻¹).

It is amazing for me to recall now the cutting jokes, the ridicule with which this result was greeted. A graduate of Harvard with a Ph.D. from Caltech, Tifft had impeccable credentials and a record of serious, careful research. Nevertheless I was treated to some lunchtime conversation at Caltech in which an influential astronomer joked (well, everyone laughed) about retroactively cancelling his degree. Tifft's home institution stood by him, however, and he has continued to produce ground-breaking research with patience and dignity.

The initial aberrant result was well on its way to being buried, however, when a few years later a rather dramatic event occurred.

Tifft was on sabbatical in Italy and happened to be lecturing on the quantization result when a skeptical member of the class said, "Here is a new list of more accurate redshifts from radio measurements of hydrogen; I am sure you won't find periodicity in here."

Not only did the quantization appear in this independent set of very accurate double galaxy measurements, but it was the most clear cut, obviously significant demonstration of the effect yet seen. It is perhaps not very uplifting at this point to hear about the lack of reaction of the astronomers who had made the measurements or the difficulty in getting the significance of the results recognized and discussed. It is still a subject carefully avoided. The results were later reconfirmed by some optical measures in the Southern Hemisphere and then very strongly confirmed *again* by the large number of accurate measures in the independent sample shown in Figure 7-3.

Figure 7-3 presents the same data as shown in Figure 7-1 except that the bins into which the data have been divided are very much smaller. This is possible because those hydrogen measures are so accurate. We see that not only are the preponderance of companion redshifts positive, but that they are quantized in the previously predicted, and previously confirmed, values of 72 km s⁻¹.

It would seem difficult, to put it mildly, to have an object with a redshift which is due to velocity and then to have this object simply disappear or dematerialize when it is not traveling at 72 km s⁻¹ or some multiple thereof. The quantization, in itself, therefore, establishes the existence of redshifts which are not caused by velocity. But, of course, there is all the antecedent proof of the previous six chapters that extragalactic objects can have redshifts which are caused by something other than velocity. The quantization is really an additional proof that at least some component of galaxy redshift can be nonvelocity.

The explanation of what is causing the intrinsic redshift, however, is made more difficult by this observational result on quantization of redshifts. For example there is no obvious reason why gravitational redshifting or photon debilitation by scattering should be quantized. The macroscopic nature of galaxies, as mentioned before, makes it difficult to imagine why all the stars and content of one galaxy could assume only certain

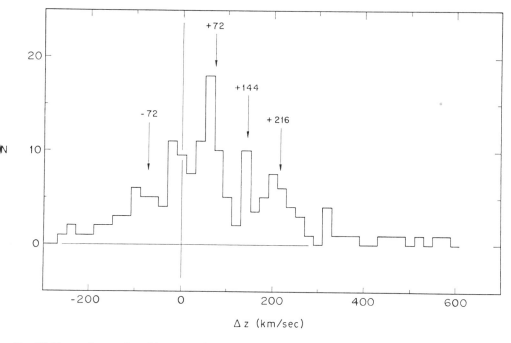

N

+72

+144

−72

+216

20

10

0

−200   0   200   400   600

Δz (km/sec)

Figure 7-3. The same diagram as Figure 7-1 except now the full accuracy of the results has been displayed in the binning. The periodic values of 72 km s⁻¹ appear clearly.

permitted values of redshift with respect to another galaxy. Unless, of course, the galaxy was at some time in the microscopic domain where quantum mechanics would be operational and could imprint on it a quantization which is inherent in the very material out of which the galaxy is made. Recall that the evidence discussed earlier indicates that quasars and protogalaxies originate in the small central nuclei of active galaxies and are expelled outward to start on their evolutionary path toward larger, more normal galaxies. If the dimensions at the origin point where this material emerges or is created are small enough, or the space-time continuum highly curved, then perhaps we would expect quantization effects associated with the birth of the galaxy to be retained or even magnified as it expands and matures. This may be a profound clue to cosmogony!

I won't apologize for the wildness of this idea because its greatest fault may turn out to

be that it was not bold enough to explain the real world. But I will say that it is an idea shared by practically no one else that I know of, even that doughty band who believe the observational evidence demands nonvelocity redshifts.

Other suggestions as to the cause of a non-velocity redshift have been made but they are all rather flabbergasted at having to explain quantization. Of course, this rather promotes a temptation to forget the whole thing. In all honesty, I must say that Sulentic and I tried to treat the quantization casually in our confirmation of it in Figure 7-3. We did not want to distract attention from the systematic positive redshifts which are so well-proven now and which demand such a radical reexamination of customary astronomical assumptions.

In all honesty, there is also another very difficult point about the quantizations. It is simply that there is such a small spread around the preferred multiples of 72 km s^{-1} that very little dispersion of real velocities is still allowable. That is, if we place a companion galaxy in the gravitational field of a parent galaxy, it should start falling in the gravitational field of the larger galaxy, it should acquire some real velocity which we would observe as a spread around its intrinsic redshift value. The spread around the observed values of 72 km s^{-1} is probably no more than ± 17 km s^{-1} as we shall see in the next chapter. This hardly seems enough velocity if the companion galaxy has stayed for any appreciable time in the vicinity of the gravitational field of the larger

galaxy. Surely gravitation should be working! Moreover, if the companions originated in the larger galaxy, they would either have to have been expelled very slowly or subsequently slowed down, because, as we have explained, their present velocities of recession from their parents cannot be very large.

So, there are problems, and much scope for theoretical interpretation. But the one thing we should absolutely never do is to ignore or renounce the observational facts because we cannot explain them. As Joe Wampler once remarked to me, "Nature is not restricted by the imagination of scientists!"

Appendix to Chapter 7

The latest paper at this writing, which also contains a review of previous evidence on small systematic redshifts of galaxies is:
1985, Arp. H. and Sulentic. J. H. "Analysis of Groups of Galaxies with Accurate Redshifts," Astrophysical Journal, 291, p. 88.

Table 7-1 in this Chapter is adapted from the article above and most earlier references in the literature can be obtained by consulting that article. Of course, there is some confusion because two papers resulting from the above paper, were published before it.
1985, Byrd, G. and Valtonen. M., "Origin of Redshift Differentials in Galaxy Groups," Astrophysical Journal, 289, p. 535 and 1985, Sulentic. J. W., "Redshift Differentials in a Complete Sample of Galaxy Groups," Astrophysical Journal, 286, p. 442.

References discussing the latest evaluation of redshifts in the Local Group and M81 group of galaxies can be found in:
1983, Arp, H., "Annual Report of the Director, Mount Wilson and Las Campanas Observatories," p. 643.
1985, Arp, H., Astronomy and Astrophysics, 156, p. 207.

CORRECTING FOR INTRINSIC REDSHIFTS AND IDENTIFYING HYDROGEN CLOUDS WITHIN NEARBY GROUPS OF GALAXIES   8

W hat every astronomer measures in the spectrum of a galaxy is the percentage by which a line is shifted from its laboratory wavelength. Astronomers habitually say they measure a velocity. That is incorrect. What they measure is a redshift, what they infer is a velocity. The only astronomer I ever knew who was meticulously accurate about this was Fritz Zwicky, who always used the term "indicative" recession velocity. For consistency with general astronomical usage we have expressed large redshifts as fractional shifts ($\Delta\lambda/\lambda$), but for smaller redshifts multiplied them by the velocity of light in km s^{-1} as if they were Doppler velocity shifts. (The speed of light is approximately 300,000 km s^{-1}).

A. Corrected Values of the Solar Motion

Even though we have consistently used the correct term—redshift or blueshift—for the measured quantity (whatever may cause the shift) we still have to remove from this measure the effect of any bona fide motions that we do know about, such as the orbital velocities of the earth around the sun and the sun around the galactic center. Redshifts of galaxies are initially measured with respect to the telescope that observes them. Then they are normaly given a small correction for the earth's motion around the sun (less than 30 km s^{-1}) and called heliocentric redshifts. The motion of the sun must then be removed.

The motion of the sun with respect to the coordinate frame of the nearby galaxies consists mainly of a rotation of the solar neighborhood around the center of our own Galaxy. In the past, this galactic rotation has usually been taken as something over 200 km s^{-1}. There is a relatively small peculiar motion of the sun with respect to the average of nearby stars: U = +9 km s^{-1} (toward the galactic center), V = +12 km s^{-1} (toward the direction of rotation), and Z = +7 km s^{-1} (out of the plane). It is also usually assumed that there is some peculiar motion of our whole Galaxy with respect to the nearby galaxies in our Local Group.

The value of all three of these motions combined, the so-called "solar motion," can only be determined relative to the average of members of the Local Group of galaxies. Gal-

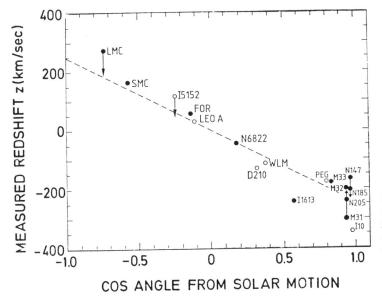

Figure 8-1. The observed redshift of Local Group galaxies as a function of their distances on the sky from the direction of motion of our sun. Filled circles represent most certain members of the Local Group, arrows indicate largest intrinsic shifts.

axies beyond the Local Group may introduce systematic motions that exist within the Local Supercluster. The value of the solar motion officially used today is 300 km s⁻¹ in a direction close to the point in the sky toward which the rotation of our Galaxy carries the sun.

But now we are faced with the first test of our finding that some galaxies in the Local Group have a component of intrinsic redshift. If we remove the effect of these intrinsic redshifts, presumably then leaving only the real velocities of the galaxies in the Local Group, will we then derive a corrected solar motion that is reasonable?

The first step in this process is shown in Figure 8-1. There we plot the observed redshifts of various galaxies in the Local Group as a function of their angular distance from the direction of motion. We see that in the direction toward which the galaxy is rotating the solar neighborhood, which accidentally happens to coincide closely with the direction toward M31, we observe the most negative redshifts. This is as expected if negative redshifts indicate velocities of approach. But! We notice that all the other galaxies in this

direction have about 80 to 90 km s⁻¹ higher redshift than M31. These are the companions to M31. Since our own galaxy is also a companion to M31, these are the same kind of galaxies as we are, and should have, on the average, no intrinsic redshift with respect to our own Galaxy. Therefore, we pass the mean line in Figure 8-1 through these companions. We see immediately that the maximum velocity of approach toward these galaxies is reduced from 300 km s⁻¹ to about 220 km s⁻¹. But this is just the modern velocity of rotation measured within our own Galaxy and therefore solves a long-standing puzzle!

The puzzle has been that by looking at the relative motions of stars and gas within our own Galaxy, we derive a rotation velocity at the position of the sun of about 220 km s⁻¹. But, as Jan Oort, the astronomer who actually made the famous announcement of the discovery of galactic rotation, remarked, "I feel some hesitation to accept as low a value as 220 km s⁻¹ because it leads to a disturbingly high relative velocity of the Galaxy and the Andromeda Nebula." The difficulty with the currently used value of the solar motion near 300 km s⁻¹ is that the peculiar motion of the galaxy, in order to add the correct amount to the galactic rotation, has to be much larger than the observed dispersion of velocities in the Local Group and has also to be coincidentally directed very nearly in the direction of M31. We see now, however, that by allowing for the observed intrinsic redshift of companion galaxies, we derive a motion of our solar neighborhood with respect to the rest of the Local Group that agrees very well with our measured galactic rotation.

In any case, the solar motion solution should have been passed through the majority of galaxies in the Local Group in Figure 8-1 rather than through M31, the single, lonely point below the line. The reason that the majority of the Local Group galaxies in this direction have been ignored in the past is that they exacerbated the already serious problem just mentioned, that of the size of the large relative velocity indicated between M31 and our own Galaxy. The problem was that such a large relative velocity was embarrassing to explain. One explanation cautiously ventured was that our Galaxy was passing M31 "like a ship in the night" (that is, it had a velocity that exceeded escape velocity from the gravitational field of the two). The trouble with this explanation is that it made our Galaxy an interloper in the Local Group and raised questions about the physical integrity of groups in general. (Note that the relative shift of M31 observed from our Galaxy is negative, exactly opposite in sign to that demanded by the expanding model of companions discussed in the previous chapter.)

Another high-level explanation that was advanced was that there is a lot of "hidden mass" in the Local Group. This is just another way of saying that your observations are explained by something you cannot observe. A little of this is all right, I suppose, but after a long time passes and you still don't observe it, and when other observations come along which do explain it, to cling to this mystical terminology seems rather absurd.

The observations which do explain it are just the systematic redshifts of the companion galaxies. We found in Chapter 7 that companion galaxies are most commonly intrinsically redshifted by 72 km s^{-1} with respect to their central, large galaxy. Since our Galaxy is a companion to M31, M31 will see our Galaxy redshifted and we will see M31 blueshifted by this amount. In fact, this is just about what we observe. From our Galaxy the shift of M31 is about –86 km s^{-1} after correction for galactic rotation . The *reason* this is so? That is the challenge. The intrinsic shifts behave as if the clocks ran fast in M31 with respect to our own (or the masses of atomic constituents were heavier). In that case, you could easily see that our Galaxy would appear redshifted from M31 and M31 would appear blueshifted from our own Galaxy. This is merely a model to help explain what the empirical observations are telling us. The possible theoretical explanations of these phenomena will be discussed later.

There is a final test we can give the newly derived motion for our Galaxy within the Local Group. We can correct all the observed redshifts in the rest of the Local Group using the new value and see if we encounter any difficulties. The result is shown in Figure 8-2. There the difference between the redshifts of each Local Group member and M31 is plotted. It is seen that the quantization into 72 km s^{-1} intervals shows up quite well!

Figure 8-2 also plots the companions for the M81 group (open circles). The M81 members all fall in the same general region of the sky, so the change in solar motion correction will not change their derived redshifts very much with respect to M81. Nevertheless, the M81 points in fact appear somewhat improved in the sense that they agree with the M31 points and both together show for the first time good confirmation of the quantization derived from the more distant groups.

We can now make a remarkable test of the previously predicted quantization interval of

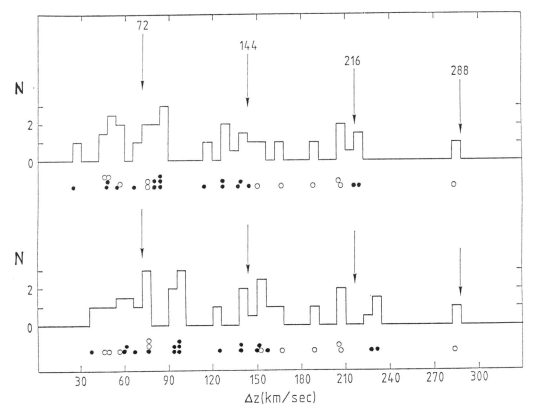

Figure 8-2. Difference in redshift between companions and main galaxies plotted for the M31 group (filled circles) and M81 group (open circles). Bottom histogram as derived, top histogram with M31 group shifted by $\Delta z = -12$ km s[-1].

72 km s[-1]. Figure 8-3 shows that if we take all the companions of the M31 and M81 groups and plot their deviation from this interval, we get essentially a normal error distribution around the value $\Delta z = 72.4$ km s[-1] (± 2 km s[-1] probable error of the mean). If there were no quantization, the points would be distributed randomly from $z = 36$ to 108 km s[-1] in Figure 8-3. If the correction for solar motion we derived by correcting for intrinsic redshifts had been wrong, it would have destroyed the concentration of differential redshifts to the value 72.4 km s[-1]!

It is important to note that a value of 72.46 km s[-1] was obtained many years earlier by Tifft from differences between redshift bands in the Coma cluster of galaxies. (The mean redshift of the Coma cluster is approximately 7000 km s[-1].) We will mention in a moment that quantization of up to 13 multiples of 72.4

km s[-1] is evident in the Local Group. If the last decimal place in that predicted and observed multiple was not correct, this agreement would not be observed.

It can be also commented that the spread in redshift around each quantized value is relatively small. For the quantization value with the largest spread in redshift, the $+72$ km s[-1] value, the average deviation is only ± 17 km s[-1]. (This is very similar to the distribution around the $+72$ km s[-1] peak found in the more distant groups—see the paper by Arp and Sulentic referenced in Chapter 7 Appendix.) In the most straightforward interpretation, this would represent companions with an intrinsic $+72$ km s[-1] shift with respect to the central galaxy, but having true velocity motions which average ± 17 km s[-1] around this value. This is a very small amount of true motion around the central galaxy. It makes

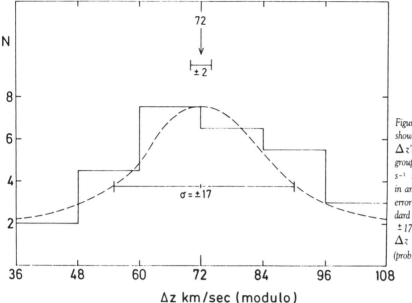

Figure 8-3. The histogram shows the distriubtion of all Δz's in both M31 and M81 groups. Folding modulo 72 km s⁻¹ shows the 29 points fall in an approximately normal error distribution with a standard deviation of σ = ±17 km s⁻¹ and a mean of Δz = 72.4 km s⁻¹ ±2 (prob. error).

for very "quiet" galaxy groups.*

In summary of this section, I would say that we have corrected for the first order effects of intrinsic redshifts in the Local Group. If there were no such thing as intrinsic redshifts this should have created havoc in the corrected velocities of Local Group galaxies. Instead, the correction solved two outstanding puzzles which for a long time have had no satisfactory explanation. One is the correct value of the rotation of our Galaxy as derived from external galaxies and the second is the large blueshift of M31 as measured from our Galaxy.

Further confirmation that this new solar motion correction is more accurate comes from the fact that we now obtain quantized values in the corrected redshift differentials within both the Local Group and M81 group galaxies. This quantization was originally found in more distant galaxies and confirmed, with independent data, by Tifft. It was confirmed again by Arp and, following that, with a very large, very accurate body of completely independent data by Sulentic and Arp. Now it has been confirmed again with quantitative precision using everyone's most accurate measured redshifts for our Local Group and M81 group galaxies. I can understand the skepticism of people in the field concerning the original results on quantization. But I cannot understand their failure to test it on further samples. Nor can I understand their continuing refusal either to accept the results of what others have found on further samples or demonstrate where the results are wrong.

---

*In the two nearest galaxy groups to us, the Local Group and Sculptor group, the redshifts of a number of galaxies are known especially accurately, with a precision of about ±8 km s⁻¹. It turns out that these redshifts are quantized into multiples of 72.4 km s⁻¹ all the way up to redshifts as high as 13 x 72 km s⁻¹ = 936 km s⁻¹.

Moreover, the average difference from the multiple values is only 8.2 km s⁻¹, implying the discrepancies are entirely due to measuring errors in the redshifts themselves. There are seven instances, however, where the redshifts are measured with greater accuracy. Here the average agreement with the 72.4 km s⁻¹ multiples is within 3 to 4 km s⁻¹! The startling implication is that these galaxy groups are "quiet" (relatively motionless) to within this astoundingly small value. Where are the motions of galaxies which should occur as a result of their falling around each other under the influence of their mutual gravity?

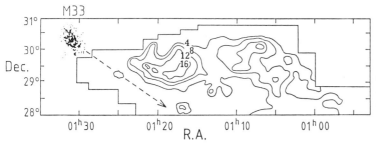

B. Hydrogen Clouds in Nearby Groups of Galaxies

Since we now have what we feel is an improved value for solar motion it is interesting to apply it to other potential members of the Local Group. The only opportunity for such an application is to re-examine certain hydrogen clouds which have been mapped over large regions of the sky, principally by the Dutch radio astronomers. These clouds are called "high velocity clouds" although in fact they have rather modest redshifts, generally in the range from -400 to $+200$ km s^{-1} (uncorrected for galactic rotation). They were briefly considered by Gerrit Verschuur to be members of the Local Group but eventually the arguments of Jan Oort prevailed that they were generally infalling into our Galaxy.

Certain clouds in the northern sky are quite large and are in a complex which extends over a large region of the sky. Since this region has a diameter of the order of 40 to 60 degrees, these particular clouds should show a systematic variation of observed redshift, a reflection of galactic rotation, if they are outside the Galaxy. Since they do not show the systematic variation, we must conclude this particular cloud complex at least is rotating with our Galaxy and is therefore part of our Galaxy. Most researchers consider it either a supernova-shell or a perturbed outer arm of our Galaxy.

The patches of hydrogen clouds which appear in other directions, however, are not generally so connected (except for the Magellanic Stream, which is a cloud chain within the Local Group). The fact that these other patches of hydrogen have generally negative redshifts, however, should not rule out their general membership in the Local Group of galaxies. This is because the center of the Local Group is generally the direction toward which our Galaxy is rotating. If hydrogen clouds were present in the center of the Local Group with redshifts relative to that center of $+200$ to -200 km s^{-1}, our rotational motion toward that direction would give them apparent redshifts of from 0 to -400 km s^{-1}. But all the hydrogen appearing in that direction with around 0 redshift will be confused with hydrogen in our own Galaxy. Hence, it might seem as if that part of the sky were filled with only negative redshift hydrogen.

Hydrogen Associated with M33.

In order to come to grips with a specific case we discuss the cloud found by M. C. H. Wright in 1974. This astronomer was deliberately looking for hydrogen toward the center of the Local Group and he found the cloud pictured in Figure 8-4. High-resolution mapping with the 140-foot NRAO radio antenna showed that the cloud was very elongated and pointed more or less directly back toward M33. Moreover the cloud narrowed down and became more intense as it approached M33. It would seem difficult to doubt that this cloud is in fact connected with M33.

Unexpected confirmation of the association of this extended neutral hydrogen (H I) with M33 is available from the measurements made by van Kuilenberg in 1970. That study shows an elongated cloud of H I stretching about 15 degrees in a west-southwest direction from the general position of M33 and about 5 degrees in the opposite direction as well. As in the cloud outlined by Wright, the most negative redshifts are on the WSW side of M33. The observed redshift for M33 is $z = -180$ km s^{-1}. The Wright cloud is at $z = -380$ km s^{-1}, that is, negative by -200 km s^{-1} with respect to M33. The van Kuilenberg detections are generally in the $-150 \lesssim z \lesssim -50$ km s^{-1} range, that is positive with respect to M33 by from 30 to 150 km s^{-1}. Since the van Kuilenberg measures cut off at -50 km s^{-1} because of possible confusion with hydrogen in our own Galaxy, we do not know whether H I exists at $\Delta z = +200$ km s^{-1} to match the H I observed by Wright at $\Delta z = -200$ km s^{-1} around M33. It would be crucial to now reobserve the H I in a slightly extended redshift range from van Kuilenberg's and with better spatial resolution, comparable to that in Wright's measures. If hydrogen is present in a -200 to $+200$ km s^{-1} range around M33 this would be strong evidence for the association of these hydrogen clouds with M33. If the distribution of gas is elongated, with negative redshifts on one side and positive on the other, it would confirm an ejection origin for the gas. If there is an imbalance toward negative redshifts it could either represent a one-sided jet preferentially directed toward us, or perhaps hydrogen which is intrinsically negatively shifted with respect to M33. If there are subclouds along the jet of discontinuous, different redshifts this would be evidence for a spread in intrinsic redshift of the cloudlets themselves.

The reason for the importance of this hydrogen cloud WSW of M33 is that an astonishing coincidence now reveals itself! In Chapter 5, Figures 5-6 and 5-7, we saw a line of quasars extending WSW from M33. The dashed arrow in Figure 8-4 shows that this line of quasars is rotated only about 20 degrees from the line of hydrogen coming out of M33. There does not seem to be any logical

way to get the hydrogen out of M33 except by ejecting it and we have already noted that the quasar alignment arises by ejection from M33. The correspondence of this line of hydrogen close to the direction of the line of quasars is dramatic confirmation of (a) the reality of that grouping of quasars, (b) their association with M33, and (c) their probable origin by ejection.

Hydrogen Associated with NGC 300

The normal logic of research would now compel us to look at the next nearest group of galaxies beyond the Local Group and see whether there existed similar hydrogen clouds to the one we have just seen associated with M33. Fortunately the observations already exist. In 1975, D. S. Mathewson, M. N. Cleary, and J. D. Murray announced a "tail" of hydrogen SE of NGC 300. NGC 300 is a large spiral similar to M33, and is one of the two dominant galaxies in what may be a separate subgroup of the extended Sculptor Group. Figure 8-5 shows the hydrogen extending away from NGC 300 in a broad jet or "tail-like" configuration. The discoverers of this feature, Mathewson, Cleary, and Murray, concluded it belonged to NGC 300 and in particular was very similar to the hydrogen extending from M33 which we have just discussed.

A rather dramatic comparison can be made by noting that the elongated cloud of hydrogen emerging from NGC 300 is roughly 3 degrees in length and reaches roughly 4 degrees from the galaxy. The elongated cloud of hydrogen coming from M33 is roughly 6 degrees in length and reaches roughly 8 degrees from the galaxy. But NGC 300 is about twice as far from us as M33, so the angular scales and placement of these two hydrogen clouds, which is inversely proportional to the distance to the galaxies, match almost exactly. The two clouds have the same size and extent!

But now an even more dramatic comparison can be made. The line of quasars which

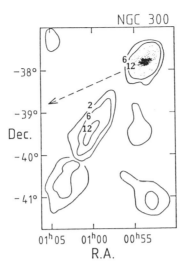

NGC 300

−38°

−39°

Dec.

−40°

−41°

01ʰ05   01ʰ00   00ʰ55

R.A.

Figure 8-5. Hydrogen southeast of NGC 300 measured by Mathewson, Cleary, and Murray. The galaxy is shown inside its hydrogen contours at the upper right. The dashed arrow points in the direction of the line of quasars shown in Fig. 5-10.

was seen extending from NGC 300 in Figure 5-10 can be plotted here in Figure 8-5. It is seen that this line of quasars is rotated by only about 25 degrees from the line of hydrogen emerging from NGC 300. But in M33 we found the line of quasars rotated by nearly the same amount, 20 degrees, from the hydrogen elongation. So, in two of the nearest spiral galaxies we find lines of hydrogen as well as slightly rotated lines of quasars pointing back to the galaxies. Moreover, we should remember that the fact that these quasars belong to these nearby galaxies had already been established by all the independent evidence discussed in the first five chapters of this book.

What are we to make of these lines of quasars and hydrogen? One might imagine a track of protogalaxies and quasars laid down in the early universe which later evolved into the various objects that we now see situated in a chain-like configuration. But that would ignore all the evidence for intermittent ejection of radio-emitting material in oppositely aligned jets from active galaxy nuclei. It would also ignore the evidence for ejection of companions in Chapter 6 as well as the evidence we will discuss in the next chapter for ejection of material from nuclei of galaxies. The observations imply instead that material

is ejected outward from the nucleus in a fairly well-collimated jet or cone of fairly narrow opening angle. What this jet contains cannot yet be specified exactly but it would be natural to assume that it contains ionized material along with some material that is either cool and/or condensed or can become so. The condensed material would be natural to identify with the quasars, and the cooler, diffuse material with the neutral, gaseous hydrogen we have now seen to be associated with the ejection. This material could all originate in the nucleus of the ejecting galaxy or, for example, the hydrogen might already exist in the outer regions of the galaxy and simply be pushed out or entrained with the outward progress of the jet. We will see in the next chapter good evidence for hydrogen in tracks and, moreover, for star formation along the edges of this ejection or in the tracks. A "beam" of material emerging from the nucleus and causing such effects in the outer regions of galaxies is well-accepted, almost conventional astronomy these days. What is new in our interpretation is that the ejected jet can contain compact bodies and, in particular, material of different intrinsic redshift.

But if material is ejected, it is improbable that this ejection direction will stay fixed forever in space. It is most likely that the ejection direction will wander, rotate, precess or move in some way. That means that material ejected in one direction will be somewhat older than material directed in another direction. We have seen evidence for this in Chapter 5 where the lines of quasars of somewhat different redshifts are somewhat differently rotated. What we have just seen in the present section is that the hydrogen is rotated to a somewhat greater degree. It would be most natural to suppose this hydrogen originated in, or was entrained in, the earliest ejection.

In any investigation where it is important not to obtain an incorrect answer one tries to find incontrovertible evidence. In court trials, for example, the jury often insists on an eyewitness account of the accused holding the "smoking gun" or some equivalent. But in the pictures we have seen with the hydrogen trailing away from the galaxies nearly in the same direction as the lines of quasars, it would seem that we have stumbled across the smoking gun.

Again, however, we are led back to the mysterious nature of the material which is ejected, the material which makes up the quasars and which exhibits the various intrinsic redshifts which are so difficult to explain. Before we come to the last observational chapter on ejection processes in galaxies, however, we should finish the subject of hydrogen clouds in nearby groups and take one last look at our Local Group of galaxies.

*Further Hydrogen Clouds in
Nearby Galaxy Groups*

We have seen hydrogen clouds associated with M33 in our Local Group and with NGC 300 the next nearest group. But we have mentioned that there are a large number of hydrogen clouds mapped all over the sky. Where do they belong? If one looks at a recent map of the sky as produced by the radio

antenna in Dwingeloo, Holland, one sees a confusion of large clouds, small clouds, and different values of measured redshift. In Figure 8-6 we have attempted to extract some sense from this plethora of data by looking at four different regions in the sky, each about 35 degrees in diameter.

The first direction we look is in the direction of the center of the Local Group, toward M31. We plot the smaller clouds and see in Figure 8-6 that they occur at both higher and lower redshifts than M31. It is unclear, of course, whether these clouds belong to M31 itself or the retinue of companions which are indicated at their ever-awkward, higher redshifts. The clouds tabulated by Hulsbosch with the Dwingeloo antenna exclude roughly the redshift region between $-100 < z < 100$ km s^{-1} where hydrogen in our own Galaxy is expected to occur. We cannot therefore know at this time about how the hydrogen clouds with relative positive redshifts balance or do not balance those with relative negative redshifts in this region.

In the next strip up in Figure 8-6 we look in the direction of the end of the Magellanic Stream (a filament of hydrogen that originates in our satellite galaxies, the Magellanic Clouds, and appears to us to sweep nearly one-third of the way around the sky). There we see two members of the Local Group, the Pegasus Dwarf and the Wolf-Lundmark-Melotte (WLM) system at redshifts somewhat higher than that of the hydrogen usually attributed to the Magellanic Stream. Since we have seen that Local Group companion galaxies have anywhere from 40 to 100 km s^{-1} intrinsic, positive redshift, they could well be actual members, or condensations in the Magellanic Stream. (Interaction filaments in more distant galaxies often show stellar or dwarf galaxy condensations within them.) But again, because the hydrogen of our own Galaxy blocks recognition of hydrogen clouds which would have positive redshifts with respect to Pegasus and WLM, we do not know

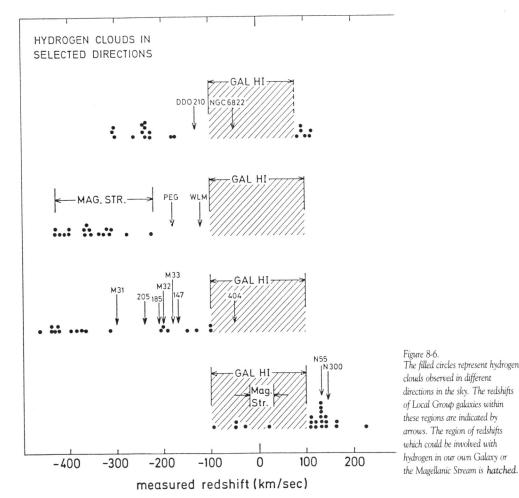

HYDROGEN CLOUDS IN
SELECTED DIRECTIONS

measured redshift (km/sec)

Figure 8-6.
The filled circles represent hydrogen clouds observed in different directions in the sky. The redshifts of Local Group galaxies within these regions are indicated by arrows. The region of redshifts which could be involved with hydrogen in our own Galaxy or the Magellanic Stream is hatched.

whether or not these two Local Group systems contribute any clouds in this region of the sky.

In the upper strip of Figure 8-6, however, we look in the direction of the Local Group members DDO 210 (David Dunlap Observatory survey of dwarf galaxies) and NGC 6822. In this direction the component of our own Galaxy's rotation is less and the Local Group members are observed at higher redshift. Here we do see some positively redshifted hydrogen clouds peeking outside the range obscured by our own Galaxy. Here, apparently, either DDO 210 or NGC 6822, or both, have hydrogen associated with them at both minus 100 to 200 km s⁻¹ and plus 100 to 200 km s⁻¹.

These panels also pretty well demonstrate that the redshifts of these hydrogen clouds reflect the amount of our galactic rotation toward that particular direction in the sky and that therefore most of these hydrogen clouds are exterior to our own Galaxy, probably bona fide members of our own Local Group of galaxies.

In the bottom panel of Figure 8-6 we look in the direction of the next nearest galaxy group, NGC 55 and NGC 300. There we are looking almost at right angles to our Galaxy's rotation, where there is little galactic rotation component, and we observe these two galaxies with positive redshifts and with a number of hydrogen clouds, closely around them of nearly the same redshift. There are also clouds of up to 200 km s^{-1} or more negative relative redshift which can be distinguished from the Magellanic Stream, which passes nearby—but not over—the position of NGC 55 and NGC 300. Knowledge of these clouds resulted from painstaking observations by Martha Haynes and Morton S. Roberts. The size, orientation, and placement, in the direct vicinity of NGC 55 and NGC 300 marks these clouds, in my opinion, as not belonging to the Magellanic Stream. This demonstrates that it would be possible with careful work to separate out the hydrogen of our own Galaxy from hydrogen in the Local Group in other directions. This must be done to better understand whether the hydrogen simply is generally in the vicinity of these Local Group galaxies or whether it has been ejected from them.

The ejection picture is supported by the fact that the clouds seem to be more frequent at redshifts of 100 to 200 km s^{-1} both positive and negative with respect to the central galaxies than at smaller redshifts. This would suggest that hydrogen clouds are separating away from their galaxies of origin with a few hundred km s^{-1}. It would also imply a relatively recent origin for the clouds—perhaps a few billion years, or about one-tenth the age of the oldest galaxies. This would fit with the relatively young age I estimate for the quasars, between about ~10^7 to ~10^9 years. But we have the problem of intrinsic redshift. If the hydrogen is smoke from the gun of the ejecting galaxy then it should center in redshift around the redshift of the ejecting galaxy. But if the hydrogen is somewhat of the nature of the ejecta it could have higher intrinsic redshift, or if of even more primeval material than the ejecting galaxy, perhaps even a net intrinsic, negative shift.

The clouds of negative-redshift hydrogen around NGC 55/NGC 300 do not seem to be matched by clouds of positive redshift. We

shall see the same result for the clouds along the minor axis of M31 in the upcoming section. This could be the result of ejections which are stronger in one direction than another. But it will require careful, systematic observation of hydrogen over a number of areas in order to answer these questions.

One point of interest before we leave the NGC 55/NGC 300 area is that there are a number of small hydrogen cloudlets just to the southeast of NGC 55. It is striking how they inhabit closely the same area as the high redshift quasars which also concentrate in this same area seen in Figure 5-10. These quasars and hydrogen do not seem to be as well aligned as the ones pointing back to NGC 300 are. It raises the question: what is the difference in the origin of these quasars if they arise from NGC 55? Does this lesser degree of alignment mean a less collimated ejection or ejection into a wider cone? NGC 55 is a large galaxy like NGC 300, but unlike NGC 300, it is rather chaotic, without the strong rotational symmetry of NGC 300.

A final comment concerns the possibility that the gaseous hydrogen has a negative intrinsic redshift with respect to all galaxies. (Or, it is perhaps easier to say all galaxies might have at least some small component of intrinsic redshift with respect to intergalactic hydrogen.) A recent study by J.H. Bieging and P. Biermann reports hydrogen observations of a sample of 39 active and interacting galaxies. A glance at their tabulated results shows several things:

First, where both optical and hydrogen redshifts are available, the optical redshifts are systematically higher. At one time, a number of years ago, a study of Virgo cluster galaxies reported no difference between hydrogen and optical redshifts. This was hailed as a reassuring proof that there was nothing wrong with the velocity interpretation of redshifts since the same value of redshift was observed for the same galaxy over the large range between the hydrogen and optical wavelengths. Now we see that is not true for at least this sample of active galaxies. The hydrogen cannot be systematically approaching us regardless of which direction we look at the galaxy. Therefore again we have a proof of the existence of intrinsic redshifts.

Secondly, the data show the most common excess optical shift averages just about $+140$ km s^{-1}. This is *another* confirmation of a major quantization peak as discussed in the previous chapter. The sample is small but the confirmation is excellent.

Finally, this represents the first hard data which tells us that when the hydrogen is present right in the galaxy, and there is a difference in redshift, that the sense is that the hydrogen has the lower intrinsic redshift. This has important implications for the hydrogen in our Local Group which has a tendency to be of negative shift with respect to the galaxies. This point should be followed up in order to answer the important question of whether just peculiar and younger galaxies have intrinsic redshifts or whether *all* galaxies could have at least some small component of intrinsic redshift.

C. The Case of the Galaxy with Superluminal Expansion, 3C 120

In the days when astronomers were first investigating radio sources, John Bolton urged me to obtain spectra of this object. I was occupied with other projects, however, and someone else got the spectrum, naming it with its number in the "3C" Cambridge Catalog of radio sources. It became a famous object and John was properly nettled that I had not observed it and given it the name it had in his discovery catalog of Parkes (Australia) radio sources. 3C 120 is a strong radio source with flat spectrum (relatively large energy in shorter radio wavelengths). It looked, on initial photographs, to be stellar, hence to be a quasar, and showed broad emission lines shifted to the red by about 10,000 km s^{-1} (ex-

pressing the shift in velocity units).

Eventually, it turned out to have the startling property that small radio features in the interior appeared to be expanding with several times the velocity of light (if the object was at its redshift distance). This was in the early days of the faster-than-light expansions and some astronomers were still a little nervous about this apparent violation of Einstein's dictum that the speed of light was a physical limit which could not be exceeded. But about this time, I made direct photographic observations of the object and showed that it was not a point source of light, but that it had a small, peculiar, resolved image with small jets and irregularities in it. The Caltech division of authoritative and supremely confident interpretation then sprang into action. They announced that since 3C 120 was a galaxy, it had to be at its redshift distance. This "fact" then proved that a few quasars which had also been discovered to have superluminal motions also had to be at their redshift distance. This hasty pronouncement was to have long lasting consequences.

The necessary rationalization finally adopted was that a relativistic jet (ejection of material at nearly the speed of light) was directed almost exactly at the observer and this then gave the illusion of faster-than-light expansion. The trouble was that (even accepting the implausible idea of ejection of massive particles at so close to the speed of light) the alignment had to be so exact that there was only about one chance in a thousand of this happening accidentally. But there were not thousands or even hundreds of objects like 3C 120 in the sky. I argued from my deepest, information-added photographs in several colors, as shown here in Figure 8-7 and 8-8 that 3C 120 was essentially a unique object. Since the outer parts of the object would look roughly the same from any direction it was exceedingly unlikely that the single object like this we had encountered would have an unresolved, inner jet accidentally pointing di-

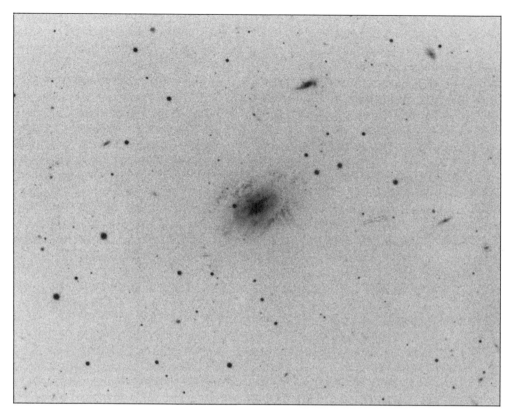

Figure 8-7. The strong radio source 3C 120 was originally classed as a quasar. Deep photograph by the author with the CTIO, 4-meter telescope shows here that it has luminous jets and filaments and material extending from the nucleus.

rectly at us. But the juggernaut paid no heed whatsoever to this reasoning.

As a matter of record, I had argued as early as 1973, in the book entitled, "The Redshift Controversy," that if we put 3C 120 out at its redshift distance, then it would be very lonely, with no other objects of the same redshift around it to form the necessary groups which we observe the universe to be organized into. At that time, I argued for its being a peculiar member of the Local Group of galaxies. But now, as old friends come back, we saw in Chapter 5 how the high-redshift, radio-strong quasars concentrated in the direction of the center of the Local Group and in the vicinity of Local Group companion galaxies. In Figures 5-6 and 5-7 we saw a subgrouping of these quasars at about R.A. = 4^h

30^m, Dec $= +5°$. Memory does not fail! That is just the position in the sky of 3C 120! Figure 8-10 shows how these quasars concentrate around 3C 120.

Other objects of various redshifts cluster about the position of 3C 120 as well. Figure 8-9 shows that low surface brightness (a characteristic usually associated with dwarfism or low intrinsic luminosity) galaxies of intermediate redshift concentrate around the position of 3C 120 more densely than in any other position in the sky.

Of great interest, because of our immediately preceding discussion of hydrogen clouds associated with members of the Local Group, are the hydrogen clouds discovered by S. Y. Meng and J. D. Kraus just flanking 3C 120 on either side.

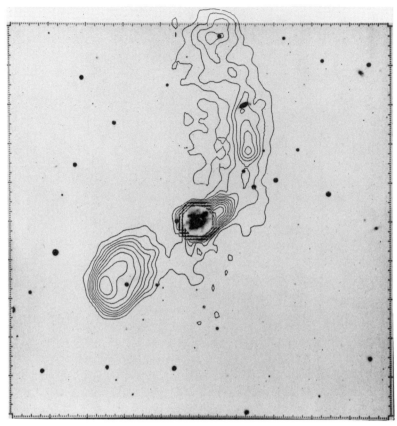

Figure 8-8. The optical image of 3C 120 with contours of ejected radio emission superposed (radio measures by Craig Walker with VLA antenna at 18 cm). Peculiar galaxy in upper right radio lobe has about 5,000 km s⁻¹ greater redshift.

Figure 8-10 shows the clustering of these various objects in the vicinity of 3C 120. Each of the three classes of objects has individually conclusive improbabilities of 1×10^{-4}, 3×10^{-4}, and 6×10^{-4} of being accidental. The compound probability of chance association with 3C 120 is therefore vanishingly small. The large scale and kinds of associations of the objects in the concentration confirms the predicted membership of 3C 120 in the Local Group. Since it is difficult to explain on conventional hypotheses the condensation of such diverse objects from an initial diffuse medium, it is obviously implied that they originated in ejections from 3C 120. Figures 8-7 and 8-8 attest to the ejection behavior of 3C 120. Perhaps, additionally, the whole ensemble originated from some low redshift, nearby member of the Local Group.

The conventional interpretation that all these objects are at the vastly different distances given by their redshift, however, would require an impossible piling up of coincidences, one on top of another. Finally, as a grand bonus for the interpretation here, if all these objects are at the same nearby distance of the Local Group, then the supposed superluminal expansions in the center of 3C 120 are not *six times* the velocity of light but only about four percent of the velocity of light, a quite precedented ejection velocity for astronomical objects.

D. A Last Look at the Local Group

The one thing that we have not done so far is to look at the region of center of our Local Group as it appears projected on the sky.

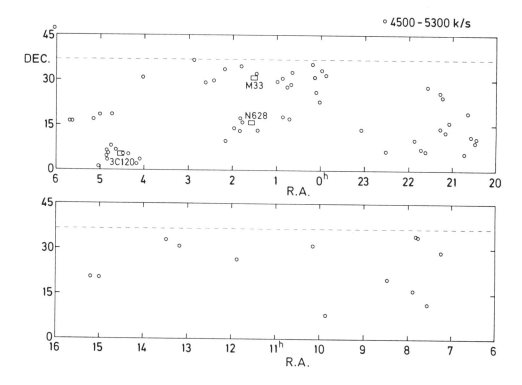

Figure 8-9. Low surface brightness galaxies from a complete survey by G. D. Bothun, T. C. Beers, and J. R. Mould are plotted in the redshift interval 4500 to 5300 km s⁻¹. Note how they clump around objects which have been claimed here as Local Group members, M33, NGC 628, and 3C 120.

Figure 8-11 shows all the certain members of the Local Group in this section of the sky (as listed in the 1985 paper which is cited in the Appendix), plus the three small clouds of highest negative shift known (from Hulsbosch's Dwingeloo survey). We see that all these objects lie along an approximately straight line that coincides closely with the minor axis of the central, largest galaxy, M31). It is amazing that this striking configuration has gone unremarked for so long.

The redshifts of these objects relative to M31 are written alongside each symbol. We first see that, as we have been stressing for the last two chapters, the redshifts of all the companion galaxies are positive with respect to M31. The shifts of the three hydrogen clouds are negative with respect to M31, yet they all lie closely along the same alignment. What

these relative redshifts mean is not entirely clear at this moment. We have decided earlier that the redshifts of the companion galaxies contain a component of intrinsic redshift so that their true velocities can have average values close to that of M31 and not drift off in back of M31 as time goes on. The hydrogen clouds may represent more recent ejection along this line of companions. But if so, we should see some hydrogen in the opposite direction with relative positive shifts of around 140 km s⁻¹. In Figure 8-6 we see some H I clouds of this shift but they are not particularly along the line to the southeast from M31, unless some of the van Kuilenberg detections of hydrogen around M33 represent this material, or unless some material of more positive shift exists, as yet undetected in the general region of M31.

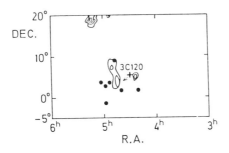

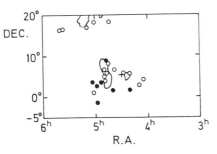

Figure 8-10. An enlargement of a portion of the sky around 3C 120 (position designated by + symbol). Top diagram shows clustering of radio quasars of z >1.35 (filled circles) and hydrogen clouds (open contours). Bottom diagram shows, in addition, clustering of low surface brightness galaxies of 4500 < z <5300 km s⁻¹ (open circles).

There are, of course, clouds of hydrogen with both plus and minus shifts with respect to M31 in all directions around the center of the Local Group. This can be seen from Figure 8-6 earlier in this section or by consulting the latest Dwingeloo map. It is unclear whether these clouds have been ejected outward from M31 in different directions, whether they have been ejected from other companions such as M33, or are simply float-ing around as general constituents in the Local Group. The objects we have depicted in Figure 8-11 seem to be the backbone of a more general distribution within the Local Group.

What does seem to be clear from Figure 8-11, however, is that most of the luminous companion galaxies and certain hydrogen clouds are very well aligned on either side of M31. What are we to make of this? One

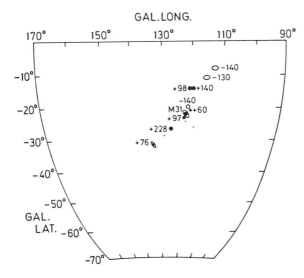

Figure 8-11. All certain members of the Local Group near M31 are plotted at the position which they appear in the sky. Redshifts relative to M31 are written next to the major companions. Open circles represent the three hydrogen clouds with the highest observed negative redshifts in the sky. The objects from lower left to upper right are: M33, dw sph II, NGC 404, dw sph. I + II, M32, M31, NGC 205, hi vel cloud, NGC 185 plus NGC 147, two hi vel clouds.

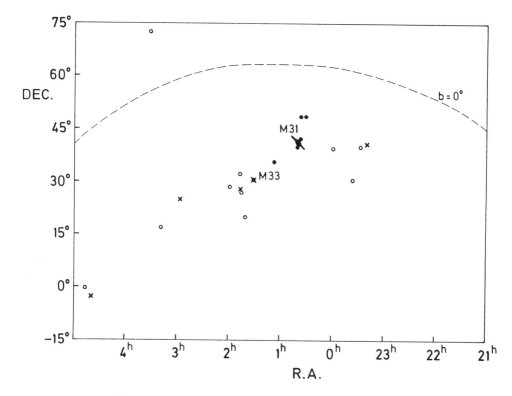

Figure 8-12. Conventional members of the Local Group (z_o < 300 km s^{-1}) are plotted as filled symbols. Open symbols (dwarfs) and crosses (spirals) represent all galaxies known which have 700 > z_o > 300 km s^{-1}. Note how higher redshift companions lie generally along M31-M33 alignment, even extending toward 3C 120 position at R.A. ≈ 4^{h}30^m, Dec + 4° 40'.

might think of the galaxies as satellites in a plane orbiting around M31 and that we see this plane edge-on. But the line is not quite straight through M31 and an orbital plane with one wing askew is not plausible. Moreover the line is fairly closely oriented along the minor axis of M31. This is the axis along which it is supposed to be easier to eject material (or if ejected isotropically, material can more easily get out along the poles rather than through the material in the plane of a spiral galaxy).

Figure 8-12 shows the disposition on the sky of galaxies just a little above the redshift of the commonly accepted Local Group members. (The higher redshifts are 300 < z_o < 700 km s^{-1}.) *It is clear that they belong to the Local Group.* This result furnishes another confirmation of the association of lower

luminosity excess redshift companions; a result forthcoming from all previous studies of physical groups of galaxies. Of additional interest here is that these fainter, higher redshift companions define the same line of Local Group galaxies through M31 and M33 as demonstrated in Figure 8-11.

This line of Local Group objects even extends down to the region of 3C 120, the very interesting Local Group member discussed in the previous section.

Do other central galaxies in groups have alignments of companions like that which we see in the M31 case? My impression is that the M31 group is unusually well-aligned. Some other groups, however, show good degrees of alignment and the general tendency is for alignment. In fact, a survey of 99 bright spiral galaxies by Sulentic, Arp, and di Tullio strongly confirmed a result that was first announced by Erik Holmberg as long ago as 1940, namely that physical companions are concentrated along the minor axis of the average edge-on spiral. The companions strung out along the minor axis of M31 as shown in Figure 8-11 could hardly provide a much better demonstration of this fact of nature first noticed by Holmberg so long ago.

Also very impressive, however, is the fact that we see many examples of chains of galaxies throughout extragalactic space. In many cases, as we shall see in the next chapter, these chains are aligned with radio ejections. There seem to be abundant precedents for the configurations to actually represent some sort of line or filament of objects.

But as we shall see again and again in these lines of objects, the redshifts cannot represent anything very close to true velocities.

In the first place, there is no systematic relationship between the redshifts at one end of the line compared to the other. Nothing obviously reflects orbital motion or currently appreciable ejection in either direction from a center. Then different kinds of objects in these lines typically have different values of redshifts. Some redshifts can be outstandingly positive. Perhaps most of all, if the objects were to have velocities corresponding to their redshifts they would move off the lines, breaking up the lines in a time short compared to the supposed age of the galaxies. The basic paradox is that apparently old galaxies exist in a linear configuration that could have lasted only a small fraction of their lifetime. The M31 line of galaxies is just the first of number in which we must try to find clues which will tell us which objects have what amounts of nonvelocity redshift.

Appendix to Chapter 8

The analysis that I made of true solar motion with respect to Local Group galaxies—once their intrinsic redshifts had been removed—had a difficult time being published. Referees did not want to permit the publication of any mention of "nonvelocity redshifts" ("hidden mass" was much more fashionable and acceptable). A rather tortured paper which minimizes references to the forbidden word "nonvelocity" finally appeared. It is:
1985, Arp, H., "A Corrected Velocity for the Local Standard of Rest by Fitting to the Mean Redshift of Local Group Galaxies," Astronomy and Astrophysics, 156, p. 207.

The basic data on Local Group membership and best current redshifts for these objects can be obtained from that reference. The analysis of hydrogen clouds which have been measured around the sky are discussed using the precepts of this chapter in:
1985, Arp, H., "H I Clouds in the Local and Sculptor Groups," Astronomical Journal, 90, p. 1012.

The very interesting data on H I in peculiar galaxies, "H I Observations of Active and Interacting Galaxies," is in:
1983, Bieging, J. H. and Biermann, P., Astronomical Journal, 88, p. 161.

EJECTION 9
FROM GALAXIES

From the first time that people started to look closely at galaxies it was clear that galaxies could eject material. By the early 1900's moderate-sized telescopes and the advent of photography had enabled individual galaxies to be examined. Among the brightest of these galaxies was M87 (Messier 87, also called NGC 4486 and, with the coming of radio astronomy, Virgo A). A photograph published by Heber Curtis in 1918 showed a luminous spike originating from its nucleus. It was like a fountain of material emerging from the center of the galaxy. It was always clear that it was ejected and it was always called the "jet" in M87.

But then it was ignored. A generation later, during the 1950's, radio astronomy began to explore the skies and immediately discovered unavoidable evidence of ejection outward from the nuclei of many different galaxies. In particular, a jet of radio emitting material was discovered emerging from the nucleus of M87. It was coincident with the original optical jet. But radio astronomers were only easy with the concept of charged particles (electrons, for example) bending in magnetic fields and therefore emitting the en-

ergy (synchrotron radiation) which they detected with their receivers. Therefore they classified the jet in M87 as "optical synchrotron" radiation, implying that it was a hot gas, would expand and dissipate and thus, if you waited a little while, the problem would go away.

This point of view ignored the optical evidence that there were compact knots of material coming out along the jet like peas in a pea shooter. It also ignored the calculations by Geoff Burbidge and others that the knots could not be supplied energy from the nucleus but had to develop energy from their own interiors. Optical photographs of the knots are shown in Figures 9-1 and 9-2. What are these objects being ejected?

At the end of the 1950's, a photographic survey of the sky appeared that had a longterm effect on the subject of galaxies. This set of photographs of about 3/4 of the entire sky was carried out with the Palomar, wide-field, Schmidt telescope. Just as the major Palomar telescopes, the 200-inch and the 48-inch, had been conceived and carried forward by the astronomers of the Carnegie Institution of Washington, so had the monumental Palo-

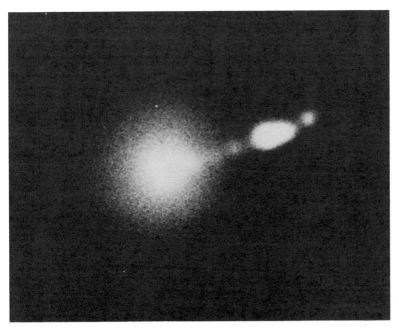

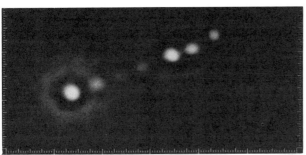

Figure 9-1. The giant galaxy M87 and its jet. Insert below shows the compact objects in jet which are more visible after resolution enhancement.

mar Schmidt Sky Survey been initiated by these same early Carnegie Institution astronomers, Edwin Hubble, Walter Baade, Rudolph Minkowski, and their colleagues. The completion of the Sky Survey enabled astronomers all over the world to study in detail what the skies really contained. One of the astronomers who looked carefully and thoughtfully at these photographs was the Armenian astrophysicist, V. A. Ambartsumian. He reported at the 1958 Solvay Conference that galaxies ejected luminous material and suggested that this material formed into, or represented the kernels of, new galaxies.

After I had later, independently reached the same conclusion from higher resolution photographs, I stumbled across Ambartsumian's 1958 report. I will always remember my feeling of deepest admiration for the clear, logical way in which he reasoned out the importance of ejection in those early days from only the small-scale photographs. Astronomers who had been at that conference told me the participants found his contribution incomprehensible and unbelievable. Later, it gained some acceptance but now has been ignored for decades.

I was not yet aware of Ambartsumian's work, however, when I started a somewhat parallel investigation. I had clearly been shut off from the newly discovered quasar field by the simple fact of not being able to get access

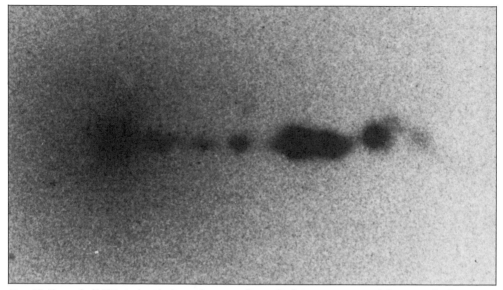

Figure 9-2. Photograph of M87 jet in ultraviolet showing that compact objects within the jet are more intense in high-energy wavelengths.

to the "secret" radio positions that were being produced mostly at Caltech. So I used my staff member's time on the 200-inch to concentrate on finishing the *Atlas of Peculiar Galaxies*.

The *Atlas* studied with high resolution the most peculiar objects that were known or had turned up on the Schmidt Sky Survey and was aimed at understanding how galaxies formed and evolved (cosmogony). It was finished in 1966 and it was then, by a twist of fate, that I was inadvertently catapulted back into the quasar game. One rainy night on Palomar mountain, I checked positions of radio sources against all *Atlas* objects. Interestingly, it turned out that many of these peculiar galaxies had radio sources paired and aligned across them as if these radio sources had been ejected. But that section of the *Atlas* which comprised the galaxies with exploding or ejecting appearance had the strongest association of these radio sources. To my utter amazement, many of these apparently associated radio sources turned out to be quasars. This discovery, as noted in Chapter 1, was the start of the long controversy, now entering its third decade, over the association of quasars with nearby galaxies.

But was it really possible that quasars were ejected from active galaxies? If so, their redshifts must be intrinsic and much larger than the velocities of ejection, since blueshifts of objects coming toward us were not observed. M87, the original ejecting galaxy, sprang to mind. It was an outstanding example of an ejecting galaxy in the center of this most active category in the *Atlas*. As we have seen, a string of optically compact, radio emitting objects emerged on a line from its nucleus. They had almost all the attributes of quasars! Only one thing was missing—the spectrum of these knots did not show any high-redshift, quasar lines—in fact, they did not show any obvious feature at all, they simply exhibited a smooth, blue continuum. Later, Sulentic and I gave arguments for their being like BL Lacertae objects, a class of quasars which, for reasons unknown, show little or no spectral features. Perhaps at this early stage in its development the chemistry of the material being ejected in M87 is so extreme it cannot even form spectral lines. In any case, M87 is clearly a key object in the mystery of why galaxies eject material and in the question of what the material can be.

A. The Giant Radio Galaxy M87

The very fact that we did not know exactly what those ejected knots were spurred me to make a number of investigations of M87. One night I had taken a deep exposure in the red with the 200-inch. The plate had been developed after lunch the next day and was sitting on the plate-viewing stand in the darkroom. To my great excitement, I noticed a linear feature on the other side of the nucleus from the jet. A counterjet! After assessing its reality, I opened the door into the hallway to see whether someone might be there to share this great moment. Fritz Zwicky was walking by and I asked him in with some trepidation because he always tended to be caustic about other people's work. He looked at the plate for a long while and finally declared, "I am glad you discovered that and not one of those other bastards." (As one comment on what could be a long story, I should say that in my opinion, Zwicky was the most creative, hard-working and renowned astronomer who worked at Caltech—but resented being reduced in observing time and excluded from councils and committees.)

But was this a counterjet to the main jet which had been so prominent ever since 1918? Further investigation showed that rather than blue continuum radiation as in the main jet, this feature was visible only in emission lines of excited gas. Moreover, it commenced further away from the nucleus and was slightly displaced from a line between the jet and the nucleus. The appearance of the counterjet is shown in Figure 9-3. Ignoring the slight misalignment for the moment, I reasoned as follows: If objects in the jet were being ejected in one direction something should be ejected in the other direction also. This would be expected in order to conserve momentum, but even more important, radio jets were generally observed to have forward and backward ejections, and M87 was

an example of a two-sided radio jet. What alternative was there to believing that a material ejection had already passed out through the counterjet side and that the emission filament we saw simply marked the track of its passage?

This interpretation was not well received. What did transpire some years later was one of those fashionable pieces of research which are temporarily admired and which so muddy the waters. More sensitive detectors were used to photograph M87 in the light of these same gaseous emission lines. The original counterjet was confirmed and some additional, fainter filaments were also found. The strongest filaments defined a line more or less along the jet and counterjet. But the whole of these observations in this new study were then suddenly used to support a currently fashionable theory that gas was condensing in the halo and "raining down" on M87. Quite misleading was the fact that the fainter wisps were pictured with boosted contrast, making it seem as if they were comparable to the counterjet feature and the other emission in the general direction of the jet.

What the fainter wisps are is not entirely clear at this moment. They might be partially the result of minor ejections or escape of gas in other than the major jet-counterjet direction. They also might be connected with "shells" around elliptical galaxies which were discovered in the *Atlas of Peculiar Galaxies*. Recently, R. Williams calculated such features could be shock waves of condensation due to periodic explosions in the nucleus.

In Figure 9-3(b), we schematically show the position of the counterjet with respect to the jet. It is seen that the lower left (SE) lobe of radio emission could have been blown slightly to the southwest by an intergalactic wind, carrying the track of the counterjet with it. On the other hand, the material to the SE could also have been ejected in a direction a bit different from that of the jet. Examination of the regions close to the nucleus

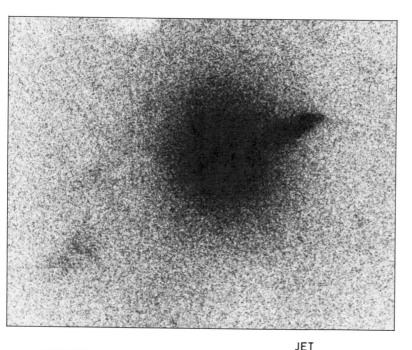

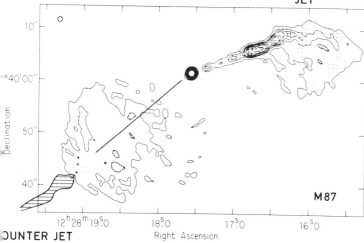

M87

COUNTER JET

Right Ascension

Figure 9-3. a) Photograph of M87 in blue oxygen emission line showing counterjet to lower left. b) Radio map of M87 shows the jet narrow to northwest and the counterjet more diffuse to southeast. The counterjet which is seen in optical emission in the upper photograph is hatched schematically and a line drawn to it from the nucleus of M87.

of M87 on the high resolution radio maps at 20 cm, and particularly at 6 cm, supports the latter conclusion. Short radio filaments can be seen protruding from M87 in the direction of the counterjet and in the opposite direction (roughly in the direction of the densest part of the fan jet which is slightly rotated from the direction of the jet). There is considerable evidence from radio jets and radio

counterjets in other galaxies that they are often slightly misaligned and often somewhat different in character. The reason for this is an intriguing, unanswered puzzle.

But the gaseous emission feature that we call the counterjet does have emission lines indicating it has been excited by some kind of mechanical shock. This supports our conclusion that the counterjet was the result of the passage of some kind of material body or bodies out along this ejection line. It also lends support to our conclusion in the previous chapter that lines of gaseous hydrogen observed to extend outward from galaxies such as M33 and NGC 300 could arise as a result of an ejection.

We will come presently to what else lies along the path of these jet and counterjet directions. But first we would like to test, in the previously mentioned spirit of research, whether there are any other objects which would support the M87 example of filaments of gaseous emission along the direction of ejected material.

B. The Giant Radio Galaxy NGC 5128

The galaxy M87 is the strongest radio source in the constellation of Virgo, hence it is also called Virgo A . What would be more natural than to look at one of the most powerful, first-discovered radio sources identified with a disturbed galaxy, namely Centaurus A? (See Introduction.) Also known as NGC 5128, this highly peculiar galaxy has two strong lobes of radio emission projecting from it in opposite directions. Farther out along these lines are enormous distributions of radio material stretching almost ten degrees across the sky and all apparently ejected from the central active galaxy (see later Fig. 9-6).

I was so sure that this galaxy would have ejection track phenomena that I pointed the 48-inch Schmidt telescope to the far southern horizon at Palomar and photographed the galaxy through emission-line filters. But the lights of San Diego made the sky too bright and I saw nothing. Some years later, the very beautiful discovery of emission filaments in NGC 5128 was made by V. Blanco, J. Graham, B. Lasker, and P. Osmer, with the then new 4-meter reflector at Cerro Tololo in Chile. The emission filaments seen in that photograph are shown here in Figure 9-4. They are narrow and point generally from the center of NGC 5128 outward in the direction of the ejected radio lobes. As in the case of M87, we see here actual, tangible evidence of passage of some entity out from the active nucleus into regions far from the galaxy.

A remarkable thing about the filaments in NGC 5128 is their extreme thinness. One inner filament is 2 arcminutes long and 7 arcseconds wide. Another, outer filament is 8 arcminutes long and has some subfilaments less than 1.5 arcseconds wide! As I commented in Chapter 3, if something is going to emerge from the active part of a galaxy nucleus, which is very small, then it too will have to be very small. Since a particle track, like an airplane vapor trail (whether it is given off from the traversing particle or a condensation in a wake), can only expand and dissipate with time, these very narrow and straight tracks in the envelope of NGC 5128 tell us that something quite small has recently passed through.

Is there a jet in NGC 5128? The Figure 9-4 insert shows that indeed a jet exists in the center of NGC 5128. It is strong and narrow, about 90 parsecs in width, and is present in both radio and X-ray emission. (Table 9-1 shows a comparison of the widths of the jets in three of the galaxies we have discussed in this book.) The jet points outward from the nucleus, closely in the direction of the narrow emission filaments just discussed (see Table 9-2). Unlike the jet in M87, no compact optical objects are presently observed along the line of the jet in NGC 5128. But it is significant to note in Figure 9-4 that the X-ray emission clumps into small knots. Farther out the emission filaments in NGC 5128 resemble more the counterjet side in M87, which we interpreted as the track of previously ejected objects.

Observations of the gaseous emission filaments in NGC 5128, as in the case of M87, tell us that these filaments have been excited by actual physical collision. (The technical term is "shock excited" and is indicated by

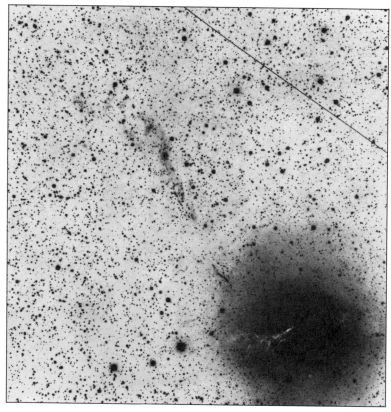

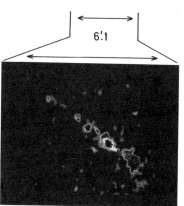

6ʹ1

Figure 9-4. The giant galaxy NGC 5128 with filaments of gaseous emission pointing out to the northeast. Insert shows the jet in the interior both in X-rays (grey) and radio (white) wavelengths.

the presence of a particular oxygen emission line which signals gas temperatures greater than can be caused by hot star radiation.) The authors who observed the spectra of these NGC 5128 filaments conclude that they are "produced within gas which is swept outward from the central parts of the galaxy." That is

rather vague, but then they are working within the conventional picture where there is a "beam of relativistic electrons which is responsible for the initiation and maintenance of the radio lobes of NGC 5128." They do not explain how a beam leads to the formation of these extremely straight and narrow filaments.

TABLE 9-1
Widths of Jets

M87	60 pc	continuum jet with compact knots
	120 pc	counterjet, representative width
NGC 5128	90 pc	inner X-ray and radio jet
	40 pc	narrowest outer filaments
NGC 1097	200 pc	narrowest jet at redshift distance of galaxy

They also avoid any reference to my prediction of tracks of compact objects passing outward, which they received prior to their analysis.

I might comment for a moment on the conventionally assumed "beam mechanism" for creating and maintaining the extended radio lobes which are seen at distances of many galaxy diameters on either side of a large number of galaxies. There is the extremely difficult and unsolved problem of inventing a mechanism which can so strongly collimate a beam emerging from the nucleus. There is the extremely difficult problem of pumping the particles in the beam with enough energy to get them traveling so close to the speed of light. Finally, there is the simple but appalling question of what happens when the beam arrives at the distance from the galaxy at which is should have an "extended lobe." The basic observation is that the energy has to go from small (cross section) to large, but rather suddenly, not gradually. The "hot spots" in the extended radio lobes are supposed to be the impact points of the beams on an external medium. But why just at this particular point? Why not farther out or closer in? And what happens when the beam rotates? The hot spots are relatively small and would be better explained, in my opinion, by compact bodies which expand or secondarily eject after a certain time. (This is the behavior we observed at the end of some of the jets in NGC 1097.) The outgoing beam may have a diffuse, ionic component but it would certainly seem to need to contain lumps of matter for which

the narrow, filamentary tracks, hot spots, and energy injection into the exterior lobes are all evidence.

C. General Alignment of Galaxies Along Lines of Radio Ejection

If compact objects are passing from the nucleus of a galaxy out into the radio lobes and perhaps beyond, can we see any concrete evidence for this in the larger regions surrounding the galaxies? The answer is an emphatic *yes*, but not exactly in a way which we might have expected. Apparently the compact objects do not remain compact.

As usual, some of the keys to the problem have been around for a long time. In 1968, it was already possible to plot the diagram shown in Figure 9-5(a). It locates all the so-called elliptical (E) galaxies in the vicinity of M87. They clearly define a line. But what is so extraordinary is that this is almost exactly the line of the jet in M87. This simply cannot be dismissed as an accident. After all, the optical jet and counterjet are confirmed by the radio jet and counterjet. The E galaxies plotted in Figure 9-5(a) were all classified by de Vaucouleurs long before I had the idea of looking at their arrangement with respect to M87, and they agree almost exactly with the line of the jet and its counterextension. We know that something material is being ejected out along this line. (We can actually see the material on one side and see the effects of passage on the other side.) Looking out along this line then, we actually encoun-

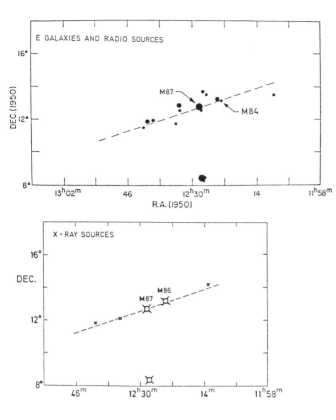

Figure 9-5. a) All galaxies classified as ellipticals (E) in the vicinity of M87. The direction of radio and optical jet and their counterextension are shown by dashed line. Strongest radio sources are marked by arrows. b) X-ray observations from an incomplete, mosaic sample over the Virgo cluster. Note that the strongest X-ray sources, including M87 and M86, fall along the line of the jet and counterjet.

ter objects which turn out to be E galaxies.

As remarked in the Introduction, the observed facts are the laws of nature, the theory must simply connect them together in some useful or satisfactory way. At this golden moment in history, I doubt that we are as sophisticated in theory as we might someday be. Nevertheless, there are certain broad inferences that we might draw from this situation.

One inference is that the E galaxies along the line originated from the compact bodies which were ejected from the nucleus of M87. But this is almost exactly the conclusion Ambartsumian came to in 1958 about galaxies in general by inspecting the then-available photographs!

Most recently an independent set of observations were made. This time it was X-rays. Coincidences again! The strongest X-ray sources so far found in the center of the Virgo cluster, although they include different galaxies, lie accurately along our line of E galaxies. This is shown in Figure 9-5(b). So, yet again, the physical reality of the line has been confirmed. These particular X-ray sources are associated with large galaxies, so it seems some of the galaxies which originated from ejection out along this line are presently active.

The comparison which cries out to be made now is: What does the larger region around NGC 5128, the other giant E galaxy with jets, reveal? Is it anything like the M87 region? Figure 9-6 (center panel) shows all the bright galaxies in a comparably sized region around NGC 5128. They also form a line! And what line is this? It turns out to be one which is close to the direction of the ejection of radio material from NGC 5128 and also to the direction of the narrow emission fila-

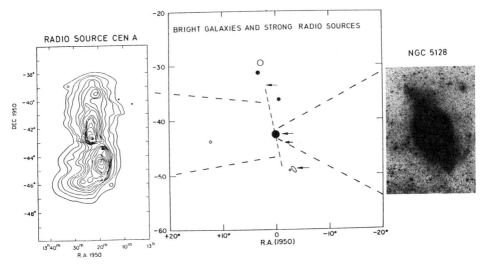

Figure 9-6. (Center) All the bright galaxies and radio sources in large area of sky around NGC 5128 (filled circles E galaxies, open circles spiral or peculiar galaxies). (Left) Radio map of the source called Cen A showing large extensions of the radio-emitting regions. (Right) Deep optical photograph of NGC 5128 showing extensions of outer regions of the galaxy, generally along the line of ejection.

ments we discussed earlier. Table 9-2 shows the continuous rotation of angle from inner to outer features which would be naturally explained by a small rotation of the ejection direction with time. The M87 ejection may have also rotated with time and thus explain the slight misalignment of the counterjet and some of the galaxies in the line (see later section).

We do not have X-ray observations over this large region around NGC 5128, so we cannot check on the alignment of X-ray sources as we did around M87. But we do have radio surveys over the area, and the arrows in Figure 9-6 show that the brightest radio sources confirm this alignment of galaxies across NGC 5128. (The brighter radio sources in the M87 region also lie along the M87 line.) If more evidence is needed, a clinching piece can be seen in Figure 9-6 (right panel) where the deep photograph of NGC 5128 shows actual material from the galaxy itself

TABLE 9-2
Rotation of Features in NGC 5128

FEATURE	POSITION ANGLE
outer line of radio material (CEN A)	0-20°
outer line of galaxies	~12°
elongation of outer luminous NGC 5128	~29°
filaments (outer)	~38°
filaments (inner)	55 ± 2
X-ray/radio jet (inner)	53 ± 1

142   Ejection from Galaxies

extending out in the direction of the outer filaments and the far outer line of galaxies and radio material.

We also note the presence of some spirals and non-E galaxies in the NGC 5128 chain. The latter would indicate a more recent origin of the galaxies than in the all-E-galaxy chain through M87. Another interesting fact is that many of the active galaxies along the line in both the M87 and the NGC 5128 cases tend to be double galaxies. Other evidence (Chapter 6) implies that more recently ejected companions show a greater tendency to be multiply interacting, objects not in dynamical equilibrium. Perhaps fissioning or multiple, compact protogalaxies are characteristic of earlier stages of galaxy formation.

D. Generations of Galaxies in the Virgo Cluster

M87 forms the core of one of the richest clusters of galaxies in the sky. In fact, the Virgo cluster is considered the center of the Local Supercluster of which our own Milky Way galaxy and Local Group of galaxies are outlying members (about 20 megaparsecs from the center). But if M87 is the most massive galaxy in the center of the Virgo cluster, why is it that only the E galaxies, massive, old systems like itself, lie along the line of the jet and the counterjet? E galaxies are supposed to consist generally of the oldest stars that we know, stars that are nearly the supposed age of the universe. So, unless the E galaxies in the line of Figure 9-5 have, for some reason, aged unusually rapidly, the presumption is that they were born far in the past. Their great age would imply that they originated from objects which were among the earliest ejections from M87. If this is so, where are the more recent ejecta and what do they look like?

Several possibilities exist. One is that younger ejecta are along this line but are undetected. They may be too faint or in the

form of something we do not consider unusual. It is also possible, of course, that ejections from M87 are intermittent and that epochs of galaxy production are widely separated. But there is another aspect which undoubtedly complicates matters. That aspect is that if the E galaxies in the line through M87 are indeed old and like other E galaxies we know about, they probably have also undergone ejection phases and created some galaxies of their own in the vicinity which are younger than they themselves are.

This expectation is confirmed if we look at spiral galaxies, which are composed of generally much younger stars than are found in ellipticals. The spirals in the vicinity of M87 form an approximately oval distribution around the line in Figure 9-5—but with the center of the oval more or less empty of spirals! This distribution of spirals was described in the earliest analyses by one of the most experienced researchers in the Virgo cluster, Gerard de Vaucouleurs.

It can be seen again in the recent work of C. Kotanyi (see Appendix). It is clear that if the secondary E galaxies along the M87 line eject progenitors of spirals in random directions, one should find a roughly hollow oval distribution of spirals, very much like the one that has actually been observed. It would be extremely difficult to explain this configuration of spirals and its location on any other grounds.

Of course—and this is where life becomes complicated in the Virgo cluster of galaxies— if its many spirals are ejecting quasars in various directions as we have seen in Chapters 4 and 5, then there may be many lines of quasars crisscrossing through this region at present. This would present a real mess for anyone trying to straighten out which quasars belonged to which galaxies. For this reason, I have always stayed away from trying to observe quasars in the Virgo cluster.

But the situation is not without possibilities. We have said that many quasars at the distance of the Virgo cluster would be too faint to be easily observed, particularly those quasars centered around $z = 1.96$. But if higher luminosity quasars are associated with the higher luminosity galaxies in Virgo they might stand out as recognizably associated. After all, one of the constant messages of the evidence we have recapitulated from the past decades is: brighter galaxies are associated with brighter quasars.

E. The Quasars in Virgo

In 1978, three objective-prism photographs were obtained with the United Kingdom Schmidt telescope in Australia. Mr. X. T. He, the talented Chinese astronomer, who so skillfully selected quasars around the jet galaxy, NGC 1097 (Chapter 4), selected the candidate quasars over the Virgo cluster region. He reported that the quasars fell closer to the bright galaxies than they did to the faint galaxies.

But the analysis did not appear in print until 1984, and then with aid of four collaborators the conclusion was put forth that they found ". . .no conclusive evidence for quasar-galaxy associations in this field. . ." Actually, inside the paper a different statement was made: that with the one-dimensional Kolmogorov-Smirnov test, "... no significant associations were found for any galaxy sample, with the exception of the 15 galaxies brighter than m = 12."

Of course, this quasar-galaxy association that we discover only after close reading, was excused as a possible selection effect in which quasars were postulated to have been missed at the edges of the region investigated. But the sample of the very brightest galaxies, brighter than m = 11, and the E galaxies, which were most concentrated to the center of the region, was not tested for association with the quasars. Most important of all, the brightest quasar candidates, those brighter than m = 18.5 and most likely to be com-

pletely detected, obviously fell very close to the center of the plate and very close to the brightest galaxies—but were not tested.

To illustrate just what was going on here we should look at Figure 9-7a. That figure shows the candidates which they tested for association with the galaxies on the plate. Pretty scattered, right?

Now look just below in Figure 9-7b, at just the quasars m = 18.5 and brighter and just the E galaxies m = 11.0 and brighter. Obviously the association of the brightest quasars in the field and the brightest, most massive galaxies in the field is so striking it needs no statistical testing at all!

To discuss for pages a technical, specialized statistical test which gives the impression of rigor—and also the implication of nonassociation—while at the same time avoiding a significant association which was predicted and is obviously present; this is not quite how I thought the scientific method should work.

The association of quasars with Virgo cluster galaxies is, however, not at all exhausted by what we have just pointed out. Two of the brightest quasars were found astonishingly close to massive E galaxies in the core of the Virgo cluster. One m = 18.5 quasar was found within 2.3 arcmin projected distance from M84 and another m = 18.5 quasar was found within 0.8 arcmin projected distance from NGC 4550. But these two galaxies are among the small number of original E galaxies which defined the line centered on M87 as shown in Figure 9-5!

Assuming a conservatively large average density of quasars, 0.5 per square degree brighter than this continuum magnitude, we easily compute probabilities (as per Chapter 1 Apdx.) of $p = 2 \times 10^{-3}$ and $p = 3 \times 10^{-4}$ for accidentally finding such quasars this close to an arbitrary point in the sky. Now we ask the natural question: What is the probability of accidentally finding these two quasars so close to members of the line of E galaxies which

THE CORE OF THE VIRGO CLUSTER

a) QUASAR CANDIDATES

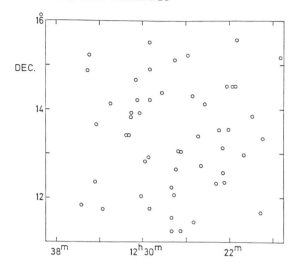

b) BRIGHTEST CONFIRMED QUASARS AND CORE GALAXIES

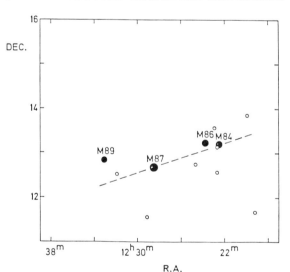

R.A.

Figure 9-7. a) Quasar candidates in the center of the Virgo cluster. b) Only the brightest (m < 18.5 mag) confirmed quasars and the brightest E galaxies in same area. Only those quasars with redshift z > 0.3 have been plotted.

were announced in 1968, as defining the core of the M87 region of the Virgo cluster? The chance of finding the closest quasar to one of these eleven (from most modern classification) E galaxies is $11 \times 3 \times 10^{-4} = 3 \times 10^{-3}$. The chance of finding the next closest is $11 \times 2 \times 10^{-3} = 2 \times 10^{-2}$. The chance of finding both in one sample is $\approx 10^{-4}$. In other words, the chance of finding two of the brightest quasars on this plate within the observed distance to the members of the M87 chain is about one chance in ten thousand!

Is it not astonishing that the authors missed this exceedingly strong confirmation of the association of bright quasars with the most massive galaxies in Virgo? Well, perhaps astonishing is not quite the right word.

Of course, there will be screams of protest

that this is statistics with small numbers and that it is *a posteriori* (after the fact) calculation. But, as we have seen from all the evidence in this book, it is not *a posteriori* but a well-predicted event. And, of course, if the probability of even just one event becomes small enough, it becomes decisive. It becomes the *experimentum crucis* which everyone claims to be seeking. The situation is reminiscent of the quasar recently found only 0.3 arcsec from the nucleus of a low redshift galaxy (Huchra et al. 1985). It was announced as a gravitational lens but if one reads beyond the abstract he finds buried inside the paper the fact that the chance of it being an accidentally lensed, background quasar is only about 2×10^{-4}. Since the chance of it being a gravitational lens is only about one in five thousand, what it actually is, in spite of the authors' evasion, is a very strong confirmation of the predicted physical association of a quasar with a galaxy. Perhaps the authors can stonewall this until their retirement. Unfortunately, some of them are quite young.

Still further anomalies are evident for the quasars in the Virgo region if one looks at the remaining observed parameter, their redshift. Strikingly, less than 10% of them have redshifts near $z = 1.96$, which is the most common redshift for quasars over the rest of the sky. What they do have is a redshift pattern shifted slightly higher than observed in the groups described in Chapters 1 and 5. One can pick out from the quasars which fall close to the M87 line of E galaxies, the following redshifts:

Observed values of redshift	Predicted with constant of redshift periodicity $\Delta \log (1 + z) = 0.098$
0.42	0.42
0.72	0.78
1.25	1.23
1.79	1.79
2.50, 2.46 (fainter)	2.50

This redshift periodicity of 0.098 which fits the Virgo quasars represents the highest interval encountered in any group of quasars to date. The evidence available so far (for example, from unpublished evidence in the NCG 520/NGC 450 region) indicates that the larger periodicity intervals go with higher luminosities. This would suggest the quasars above are the highest luminosity group observed so far. Such a result would be appropriate since the Virgo cluster galaxies are among the most distant groups we have considered so far. About five other quasars in the vicinity of the M87 line have redshifts near $z \approx 2.2$. It is not clear whether they are foreground quasars, contributed by other galaxies in the area, or represent dispersion in the properties of the quasars in the line. The answers to these questions will require complete, systematic observing programs, not the present small, incomplete samples which take many years to publish and religiously force the interpretations into the canonical assumptions.

In any case, we have seen that when we actually look at the data so far available, the predictions of association are supported in that high luminosity kinds of quasars are associated with the high mass galaxies in the Virgo cluster.

Chains of Galaxies

We have just seen lines of galaxies associated with M87 and NGC 5128. It is a curious and exciting property of the universe that a great deal of extragalactic matter appears to be arranged in linear formations. For example, in order to establish another proof of the reality of the lines of galaxies through M87 and NGC 5128, I investigated the 14 brightest radio sources in the sky, including Virgo A and Centaurus A, which are associated with bright galaxies. Almost all were found to occur in chains of galaxies, and in most cases where radio ejection was defined, the line of radio emission coincided with the line of galaxies. Even though this result has been carefully ignored since 1968, there can be no reasonable interpretation other than that the galaxies in these lines have arisen from an ejection process in the central galaxy. To extract from my 1978 article in the Ambartsumian celebration volume:

Of course, the galaxies in these lines are not generally very compact. This forced the conclusion that the progenitors of these galaxies had been, and that they had expanded and evolved into normal galaxies. Compact objects of the kind we have been discussing as ejecta are characteristically active and would be expected to expand into a somewhat more relaxed system. In fact, we would expect, and do observe, secondary activity on the part of these ejected bodies on a scaled-down version but very much like that of the initial parent bodies. The picture which emerges then is that initially compact, ejected bodies expand and secondarily eject, probably accompanied with gas, dust, and star formation and become small active galaxies. As time goes on they are hypothesized to perhaps grow larger still, but in any case to come more into equilibrium, evolve into more relaxed, older-type galaxies. What other conclusion is available other than that these compact, ejected galaxy progenitors are, in fact, the quasars?

Although they are much less massive than the giant galaxies M87 and NGC 5128 that we have just discussed, the implication is that the line of companions emanating from M31 in the Local Group (shown in Fig. 8-11 and 8-12) also arose by ejection some time in the past. As mentioned in the discussion, the ejection would be more or less along the present minor axis of M31, a natural place for an ejection to break free in a galaxy with rotational symmetry. In this connection, I well remember seeing a radio map of M31 made with the large radio telescope in Holland. It showed a considerable number of small radio sources emerging in a sort of "S" configuration in both directions along the minor axis of M31. The astronomer who showed it to me was extremely nervous about this unanticipated and not readily explainable result. I felt at the time that this important result would somehow escape the glare of publicity, and, indeed, it goes quite unremarked today. It would seem that ejection and counterejection is a general physical phenomenon that operates over an enormous range of length scales in the universe. It is seen here in the structure of the largest groups and clusters of galaxies, it is seen down to the smallest individual stars in formation (T Tauri stars and Haro-Herbig objects), and probably in the tiny, degenerate neutron stars known as pulsars.

Of course, it is not clear whether all chains of galaxies result from ejection processes. Perhaps some arise because matter originally condensed in filamentary structures in the early universe. The latter is the usual assumption of conventional astronomy. But if some chains arise by ejection perhaps all the extragalactic matter in the universe unfolded first from a few active centers and then further from secondary and perhaps even tertiary centers. This concept would be worth investigating with an open mind. But regardless of their origin, chains and filaments of galaxies are very common features of the distribution of galaxies on the sky.

Jan Oort was the first to comment (to my knowledge) on such structures on this large a scale, involving clusters and superclusters. In the recent *Catalog of Southern Peculiar Galaxies and Associations* by Arp and Madore one of the most populated categories was "chains—4 or more galaxies aligned." One of these examples of chains of galaxies from that catalog is shown in Figure 9-8. These aligned structures also represent an insoluble paradox for the conventional view of redshifts:

The point is that the redshifts of the **chain members differ sufficiently that if they are interpreted as velocity, the chains will fly apart in a time much less than the presumed age of the galaxies.** In the chain of companions which goes through M31 one can easily see not only that the companions are system-

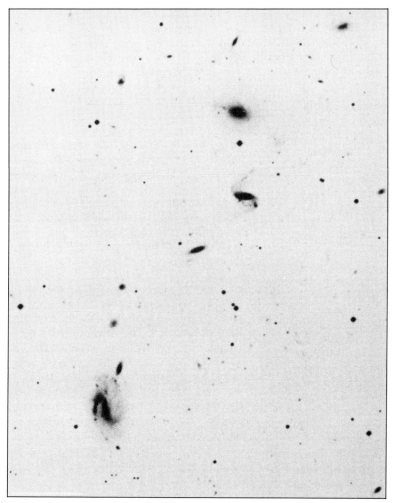

Figure 9-8. A chain of
nonequilibrium-form galaxies.

atically shifted with respect to M31 but also
that they differ from each other by the order
of 100 km s⁻¹. In the line of E galaxies through
M87 the range of redshifts is about $\Delta z = 3,000$ km s⁻¹—a veritable explosion away from
the line—all involving galaxies which are
supposed to be among the oldest we know, of
the order of 10^{10} years old!*

Obviously we have another proof that
the redshifts cannot be due only to velocity
but must contain varying components of intrinsic redshifts. That is, if the lines are real. I
will leave it to the reader to judge whether
the lines are real or just random, meaningless

accidents. He can consult Figures 8-11 and 8-
12, 9-5, 9-6, and 9-8. Further references are
given in the Appendix. In the future, the
study of redshifts in chains of galaxies would
provide a very fruitful opportunity to study
the relationship of excess redshift with type of
galaxy.

In fact, it is my opinion that the study of
chains of galaxies on the sky will force the
most unexpected and drastic revolution in
understanding of galaxies and their place in
the universe. If, for example, galaxies with
redshift between $3100 < cz_0 < 5100$ km s⁻¹
are plotted, it is seen that they form one huge

---

*At 1000 km s⁻¹, a galaxy would move 10 megaparsecs in 10 billion years—half the present distance from our Galaxy to M87.

filament stretching more than 40 degrees across the sky. This filament is centered on the bright, relatively nearby Sb spiral, M81. Investigation of all the brightest apparent magnitude galaxies in the northern sky shows 13 out of 14 in uncrowded regions have similar lines of high redshift galaxies emanating from them. The origin of these lines would seem to be by ejection. The explanation for the high redshift, physical nature and origin of the galaxies in the lines may eventually make present-day astronomy appear more primitive than Ptolemaic astronomy ever seemed.

G.Systematic Redshifts of Radio Galaxies and Spirals

There are already some well-established correlations of certain kinds of galaxies with excess redshift. For example, there is a correlation of intrinsic redshift with radio emission in galaxies. This appeared more than 12 years ago when Tifft pointed out that radio galaxies in the Coma cluster of galaxies have mean redshifts about 700 km s^{-1} greater than the mean of the rest of the nonradio galaxies in the cluster. Later, Sulentic showed the same to be true in Virgo. The latest and most complete survey of radio galaxies in the Coma, Virgo, and Hercules clusters by E. Valentjin provides unequivocal evidence that the radio galaxies in all these clusters have significantly higher redshifts on the average. Of course, this result by itself, immediately establishes the existence of nonvelocity redshifts.

The consequences for the groups and lines we have been studying is the following: If the largest central galaxy is reasonably radio-quiet, then it is observed to be the lowest-redshift member of the group and the companions, as in the case of M31-like groups, are preponderantly higher in redshift. But if the largest galaxy is a radio source, then there is a counter-tendency for it to be of higher redshift than the rest of its group. This

can be seen in the case of M87, the largest galaxy at the center of the line of galaxies, but also a very strong radio source. It is many hundreds of km s^{-1} higher in redshift than the average of the remainder of the galaxies in the line. We must therefore be careful in analyzing any group to notice what kind of galaxy the dominant galaxy is, and to try to separate the effect of its type.

Another correlation of intrinsic redshift with galaxy type appears in the difference in intrinsic redshift between spiral and elliptical galaxies. This important effect was pointed out by T. Jaakkola in 1971 and again in 1973. For pairs, groups, or clusters, whenever galaxies are at demonstrably the same distance, the spirals have systematically the higher redshift. This has been proven many times over in some of the references listed in Chapter 7. The latest demonstration is from the work of Edmond Giraud. The data in Figure 9-9a clearly show the Sbc and Sc spirals in a wide range of groups have more than 100 km s^{-1} excess redshift. Of course, an even larger effect had already been demonstrated in clusters of galaxies as shown in Figure 9-9b.

This effect furnishes, by itself, another proof of nonvelocity redshifts. The effect is conspicuous in a cluster such as Virgo where the bright spirals have redshifts from hundreds to thousands of km s^{-1} greater than the ellipticals, in spite of the fact that they all obviously form one cluster. The attempts to get around this have been, in my opinion, rather disreputable. In the Virgo cluster, for example, as the spirals become later in type (that is, less regular structure, more like irregular Sd and Sm class) they also become progressively less luminous and more numerous. In other words, they are no longer spirals, they are dwarf galaxies. By adding large numbers of these lower redshift dwarfs into the limited number of more massive, true spirals, some investigators have made the spiral-elliptical redshift difference go away. At a recent conference on the Virgo cluster, I pointed out

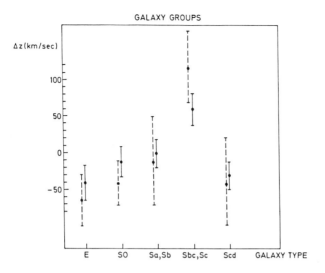

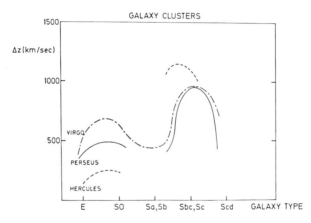

Figure 9-9. a) The intrinsic redshift of spiral galaxies in physical groups (from E. Giraud). b) The intrinsic redshift of spiral galaxies in large clusters (Moles, Nottale, Giraud).

that it was dishonest to fudge the data in this way. After listening carefully to this, the summarizer of the conference got up and said that he was glad to see this troublesome effect had finally gone away thanks to better data!

How should we reconcile the excess redshifts of radio galaxies and spiral galaxies with the excess redshift of companion galaxies that was discussed in Chapter 7? The nature of companion galaxies might suggest one explanation. Companion galaxies, if formed as a result of more recent ejection from a larger galaxy, should be younger. Even if formed by other means, spiral galaxies contain a higher percentage of younger stars than galaxies in general, which implies they also may be formed at a more recent epoch than other galaxies. Observationally, galaxies with older stellar populations tend to be in the center of clusters and groups while the spirals appear preferentially toward the cluster edges where they would naturally travel if ejected from older central galaxies. Spirals are less massive, of course, than E galaxies of comparable apparent brightness. Spirals therefore tend also to be companion galaxies in a mass sense. Moreover, if both companions and spirals tend to be younger than average, they may

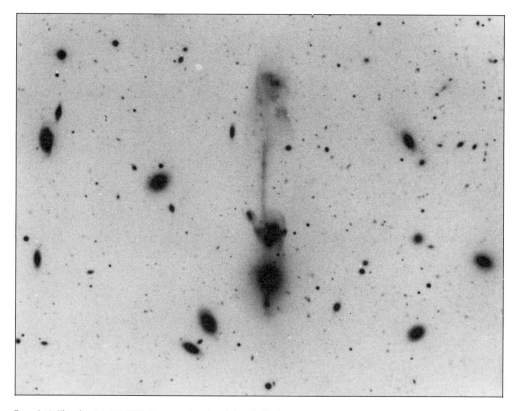

Figure 9-10. The galaxy is NGC 3561. Ejection north and south from the E galaxy is evident. The counterjet appears to have punctured a neighboring spiral. The nearest stellar image to the west of the E galaxy is a quasar of redshift near 2.

also tend to be more active in the sense of proclivity for radio ejections or explosions. In all then, characteristics of youth and activity would be empirically linked, in my mind, with the excess redshift.

H. Ejection from Spiral Galaxies and the Possibility of Spiral-Arm Formation

We have seen that the largest E galaxies known, M87 and NGC 5128 (the radio sources Vir A and Cen A), conspicuously eject material. We have mentioned that systematic studies show that E galaxies generally can erupt at least from time to time. An example of a fainter, and presumably more distant, E galaxy ejecting material is shown in Figure 9-10. We see the short ejection south-

ward from the E galaxy, but the counterjet in the opposite direction would probably be invisible if it were not for the fortuitous placement of the spiral galaxy in the path of the counterjet. As it is, we can now see the counterjet puncturing the spiral and creating a spectacular plume out along the line of ejection. Of course, a ubiquitous quasar is nearby, the nearest stellar image to the west of the E galaxy.

Not just E galaxies, but other types of galaxies as well, can eject material. In fact, there is evidence that ejection phenomena occur on many-sized scales and in many objects in the universe.

Bipolar outflow from objects believed to be associated with star formation in our own Galaxy is one example. SS433, the extraordi-

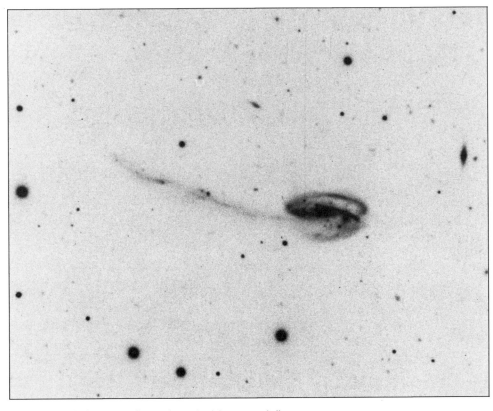

Figure 9-11. A spiral galaxy ejecting a filament of material and showing a recoil effect.

nary star that is interpreted as ejecting luminous material near the velocity of light, is another example. But of most interest here are the narrow, collimated ejections from spiral galaxies as illustrated by the example in Figure 9-11. If an object were falling into the galaxy pictured in Figure 9-11, it would require an interacting medium to produce the pictured track. Since such a medium is unlikely, we conclude it was ejected, perhaps from the disrupted point visible on the one spiral arm. This ejection is probably the same event that gives the galaxy a "recoil" appearance. Note the narrow, more or less constant width of this filament over its relatively long extension.

As we saw in the spiral galaxy with jets discussed in Chapter 4, however, ejection in the plane of a spiral provides the most infor-

mation because of the effects which it can have on the gas, dust, and spiral arms, all of which are situated in that plane. An extremely important example of this was discussed by P. van der Kruit, J. H. Oort, and D. S. Mathewson in 1972. As Figure 9-12 shows, two curved filaments of *radio emission* emerge from the nucleus of this large, nearby spiral galaxy, NGC 4258. These are not the spiral arms seen in visible light! The normal spiral arms of blue stars and emission regions are off at another angle emerging from the nucleus.

What is in the position of the radio arms? Precisely what we saw in the direction of radio ejection from M87 and NGC 5128—gaseous emission filaments. The emission filaments were discovered in 1961 by the elegant photographic techniques of G. Courtes and P. Cruvellier. The authors of the later ra-

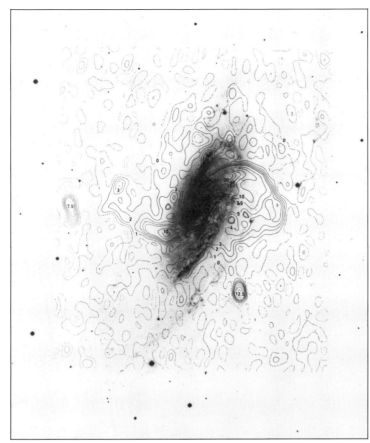

Figure 9-12. The spiral galaxy NGC 4258 showing ejected radio arms emerging from the nucleus along a gaseous emission filament—probably the start of a new set of spiral arms or a residue of old arms.

dio measures suggest the emission filaments and radio arms were caused by ". . .clouds" expelled from the nucleus in two opposite directions in the equatorial plane about 18 million years ago, at velocities ranging from about 800-1600 km s^{-1}.* In addition to this example, it is also true that the spiral galaxies with very energetic nuclei (the so-called "Seyferts") show evidence of jets emerging from their nuclei (NCG 1068 and NGC 4151 are two examples.)

The observations really tell us two things. First they show that spiral galaxies can undergo much the same kind of ejection behavior as we have seen in the giant, radio-emitting E galaxies. This makes sense because both the E galaxies and spiral galaxies can have active nuclei and active nuclei are undoubtedly the source of the ejections. A difference, however, is that spiral galaxies have disks which are in rotation and any linear markings in the plane are going to be quickly curved into a spiral shape by the differential (outer radii lagging behind inner) rotation in the plane of the disk.

In fact, this last conclusion suggests a general explanation for a long-standing puzzle. Ever since people could see that a large class of galaxies had symmetrical, usually paired, spiral arms, one question has been outstanding: What causes spiral galaxies? What causes spiral arms?

* In addition two recent observations by J. R. Roy and R. Aresenault show the gaseous emission in the southeastern radio arm is very broad—i.e., contains an unusually large range of redshifts. Does this represent a range of velocities in this protoarm? This is a key object in which to elucidate the process of spiral arm formation.

Ambartsumian advanced the idea, in 1958 and again in 1964, that ejection from the nucleus of a galaxy could produce the type of disturbances that would lead to the formation of spiral arms in galaxies. S.S. Huang and Paris Pismis independently proposed this concept in 1960. In 1969, I argued from the morphological evidence and from examples of peculiar galaxies that ejection indeed is the general cause of spiral structure. The observations of NGC 4258 just discussed bolstered this explanation with a specific example of a proto (gaseous emission) arm forming as a result of an ejection. The astronomers who recently made the observations in NGC 5128 demonstrate that actual star formation takes place along emission filaments which we concluded were caused by recent ejection. (Spiral arms are characterized by their young, hot bright stars; that is, by the occurrence of relatively recent star formation.) With gaseous filaments and star formation, we have all the ingredients for spiral-arm formation. We only need now the differential rotation of the gas already in the disk to feed rotational angular momentum into the arms and shear them into their characteristic spiral shape. Perhaps the magnetic field lying along the curved spiral arms turns ejection velocity into rotation velocity. Finally, at this point perhaps the conventional mechanisms of density wave compression and stochastic (random walk) star formation in the spiral arms takes over.

We see there are observational grounds for believing that the ubiquitous and lovely spiral arms which are seen in so many galaxies are actually caused by the ejection of material from the nucleus of the galaxy. Perhaps the arms are the tracks of the same ejections that mark the birth of the quasars.

One final comment: We have seen companions of spirals, which have been suggested to arise by ejection, aligned in minor axis directions. We have also seen evidence for ejection in the plane of rotation of spirals (at right

angles to the minor axis). In which directions then do spirals eject? Well, perhaps they can eject in any direction. When it is along the minor axis, the ejecta escape out of the plane without significant interaction. When ejection occurs in the plane, the ejection gives birth to spiral arms and—because the ejecta are slowed by their interaction with material in the plane—they do not escape very far from the originating galaxy. What should we expect in this latter case? Why, companions on the ends of spiral arms, in some cases! But this is just the special class of objects in the *Atlas of Peculiar Galaxies* as shown in Figure 6-1, which started off the whole subject of companions with excess redshift.

What else is ejected besides proto-companion galaxies? We have seen hydrogen with unusual redshift along the minor axis of M31, and hydrogen in a line from M33 and NGC 300. If we look roughly to the east of the ejecting galaxy, NGC 4258, we see a long, straight string of neutral hydrogen stretching 30-50° across the sky from NGC 4258: (Dwingeloo maps). But if this hydrogen is associated with NGC 4258, it has a redshift 500-600 km s^{-1} more negative than the galaxy. Of course, NGC 4258 could be a more nearby galaxy than we think with an intrinsic redshift of this order. Still it would leave this hydrogen somewhat negative in shift, with reference to our own galaxy. If the shift of hydrogen in the Local Group turns out to be systematically, intrinsically, negative, however, the identification of this string with NGC 4258 might be worth considering.

I. The Spiral Galaxy with Three Quasars, NGC 1073

In the first part of Chapter 1, I introduced a spiral galaxy with three quasars so close as to have a negligible chance of being accidental. We saw in Chapter 5 how, despite the large differences between the redshifts of these quasars, they all fit exactly the periodic-

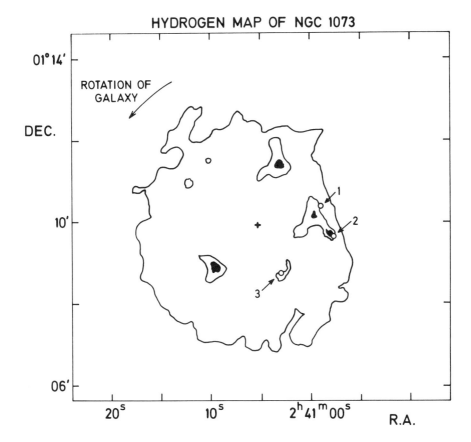

HYDROGEN MAP OF NGC 1073

Figure 9-13. Map of the neutral hydrogen in NGC 1073 (see Figure 1-2). Three small circles show the locations of the three quasars when rotated forward by 20 degrees.

ity relation which the majority of quasars exhibit. But there has never been any tangible evidence of interaction between these quasars and the disk of NGC 1073 which they are seen projected against. It was therefore with great interest that I looked at the map of neutral hydrogen over the face of NGC 1073 which Stephan Gottesman recently produced with the aid of the most powerful instrument for detailed radio observations, the Very Large Array. Some of the contours from that map are reproduced in Figure 9-13.

Disappointingly, nothing unusual appears in the map at the projected position of the three quasars. But on closer inspection one sees three concentrations of hydrogen in the west side of NGC 1073 in a pattern which resembles the distribution of the three quasars. If one then "rotates" the three quasars forward, in the direction of rotation of the galaxy, lo and behold, the three quasars then coincide closely with these three lumps of hydrogen! We suddenly remember that the galaxy is rotating! The reader can judge the fit himself by looking at the position of the small circles in Figure 9-13.

What can this mean? If we recall our consistent picture, a very compact, protoquasar-like body is ejected from the nucleus of a galaxy. We realize that if any diffuse material is ejected with this body that this diffuse material will interact with the hydrogen in the disk of the galaxy if the ejection travels out in the plane. This can either be hydrogen from the inner regions of the host galaxy carried outward or hydrogen already in the outer regions compacted by the ejection. The important point is that the material already rotating in the outer disk then carries this hydrogen lump forward in the direction of rotation, leaving the compact protoquasar behind. The resulting separation depends somewhat on the speed and interaction cross-section of the diffuse material accompanying each quasar, so we would not expect perfect correspondence in position. But since small galaxies rotate about once every 2×10^8 years, we would expect a $20°$ rotation in about 10^7 years. This is just the time scale we obtained for the quasars being ejected from NGC 1097 in Chapter 4. It also suggests another mechanism for obtaining the angular rotation between the lines of quasars and the ejected hydrogen clouds in M33 and NGC 300.

There is a flattened edge to the hydrogen outline of the galaxy beyond the two westernmost quasars. This is peculiar, and we might speculate that an ejected body farther out had exploded, pushing back the hydrogen toward the quasars we see, or even, perhaps there has been some gravitational infall toward the quasars. This would clearly seem to be one of the highest priority objects for further intensive study.

To summarize: the most important feature of the hydrogen newly observed in NGC 1073 is that some of the concentrations appear to bear a significant relation to the quasars. This is additional, and now direct, proof of their association with the galaxy. Almost as important, the quasars lag slightly behind the hydrogen concentrations in a way which confirms our expectations from previously discussed examples of ejection in the plane of a spiral galaxy. From the standpoint of the general origin of spiral structure, it is interesting to note that all three quasars in NGC 1073 lie along the general line of major spiral arms in the galaxy.

J. Ejection and X-Rays

For the final section of this chapter, I wish to develop further the close relationship that exists between ejections, quasars, and X-rays. On the one hand, this furnishes further proof of the association of quasars with large galaxies and, on the other hand, offers the opportunity to gather more physical data concerning this mysterious process of ejection and on the mysterious nature of the quasars themselves.

It has become clear since the advent of X-ray astronomy from earth-orbiting satellites that ejection activity in galaxies is characteristically accompanied by X-rays. The knots in the jet of M87 are X-ray sources, there is an X-ray jet in the nucleus of NGC 5128 pointing out along the line of ejection shown in Figure 9-4, and an elongated region of X-ray emission emerges from the active center of the spiral Seyfert, NGC 4151.

A striking example of X-ray-emitting material associated with ejection is in the jet galaxy, NGC 1097, which was discussed in Chapter 4. Figure 4-4 of that chapter shows how this X-ray material is distributed predominantly outward from the nucleus of NGC 1097 between and along the two strongest jets in the N, NE direction. One can see plainly that this X-ray material is continuously distributed from the galaxy out into the region of the jets. The inner X-ray material in the galaxy is also concentrated over on the side of the strong jets (as is the radio material). Even the ratio of high energy to low energy (the hardness ratio) for these X-rays changes continuously from inner to outer regions in NGC 1097. Figure 4-4 also shows that various pieces of this X-ray emission in the outer regions of the jets are identified with quasars. Since all this X-ray material obviously belongs to the galaxy, this is rather stunning proof that the quasars are associated with the galaxy, and have been ejected from the nucleus. This fact has gone absolutely un-

THE GALAXY CLUSTER ABELL 1367

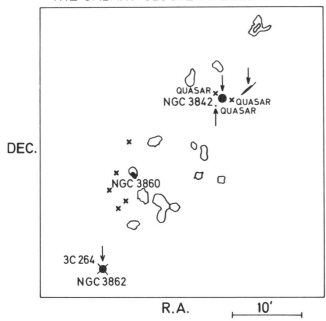

DEC.

R.A.   ⊢——— 10' ———⊣

Figure 9-14. Map of Abell 1367, a cluster of galaxies like the Virgo cluster. The irregular outlines represent extended X-ray emission, many of which are associated with galaxies, and the crosses designate point-source X-ray emissions. Arrows point to radio sources. The two closest X-ray sources to NGC 3842 are the quasars shown in Figure 1-1.

commented on by the other side of the controversy. But then, what could they say?

Are there other cases which support this association of X-ray material with ejected quasars? There are. We saw also in Chapter 4 that the exploding galaxy NGC 520 had a line of quasars emerging from it. There is a lot of X-ray material scattered around NGC 520 and the outer portion of this material is elongated along the direction of the line of quasars. As in the case of NGC 1097, some pieces of this X-ray emission are identified with confirmed quasars. Since I have been warned against using this X-ray map "without permission" I will not show it here but merely refer the interested reader to the 1983 Liège Conference Proceedings where an approximate rendition, with quasars, was published.

Perhaps one of the most convincing proofs of the association of quasars and X-ray material with galaxies now comes from the galaxy first discussed in this book, NGC 3842. That galaxy had three quasars so closely spaced around it that there was less

than one chance in a million of it being accidental. The quasars were discovered because the brightest two were strong X-ray sources.

It turns out that NGC 3842 is a member of a cluster, Abell 1367, the only cluster known to have X-ray properties like those of the Virgo cluster. Many of the individual galaxies in these two clusters are sources of X-ray emission instead of the more usual case where a diffuse X-ray medium dominates the cluster. Figure 9-14 shows that A1367 has many features similar to the M87 region of the Virgo cluster. A1367 contains a bright E galaxy, NGC 3862, which is a strong radio and X-ray source. In these respects NGC 3862 is similar to M87.

In A1367 we see an elongated distribution of X-ray galaxies reaching from NGC 3862 over to another E galaxy, NGC 3842, which is also a radio source. This latter configuration is similar to the Virgo cluster line that extends through the E galaxy M84 as shown in Figure 9-5. Now, it is just around the radio E galaxy, NGC 3842, that we find

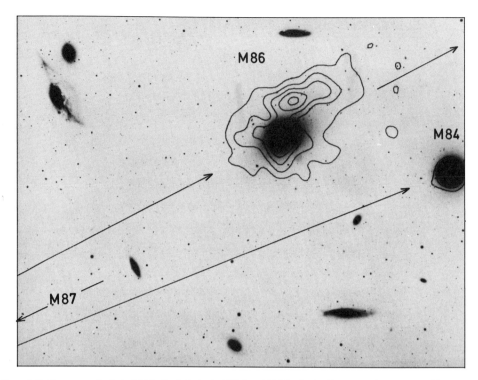

Figure 9-15. X-ray maps of individual bright E galaxies in the M87 line. (a) M86, showing X-ray material streaming roughly away from the direction to M87.

the X-ray quasars, as if they had been ejected out on either side of the galaxy. But the radio E galaxy M84, which is in a similar position in the M87 line, also has a strong X-ray quasar very close to it. We saw in a preceding section that the strong X-ray quasar was so close to M84 that there was only about 2×10^{-3} chance of it being accidental (actually much less chance for an X-ray quasar because there are far fewer strong X-ray quasars than there are quasars.)

Therefore, A1367 and NGC 3842 provide a rather detailed confirmation of what we saw in the M87 region, alignments of galaxies, radio sources, X-ray sources, and associations of quasars with these lines.

Now that we have again mentioned M84 and the M87 line of galaxies, it is instructive to examine detailed X-ray maps of some of the galaxies in the line as shown below in Fig-

ure 9-15. The first map shows that the X-ray halo around M86 is streaming off in a WNW direction, as if a wind were blowing from the general direction of M87. But what is even more significant is that M84 lies almost exactly along the line of the jet from M87. Figure 9-15 (b) shows that its X-ray isophotes are compressed as if M84 were moving, through a medium, in a direction away from M87 *exactly* along the line of the jet! Even the X-ray astronomers who derived the X-ray map said that it looks as though M84 is moving to the west through the medium of the Virgo cluster. Not exactly west. Just exactly along the line of the jet from M87 as Figure 9-15 shows! It *must* be clinching proof to remember that in 1968, 17 years before the X-ray measures, it was concluded from the evidence available that M84 was one of the galaxies which had been ejected from M87 and therefore must be

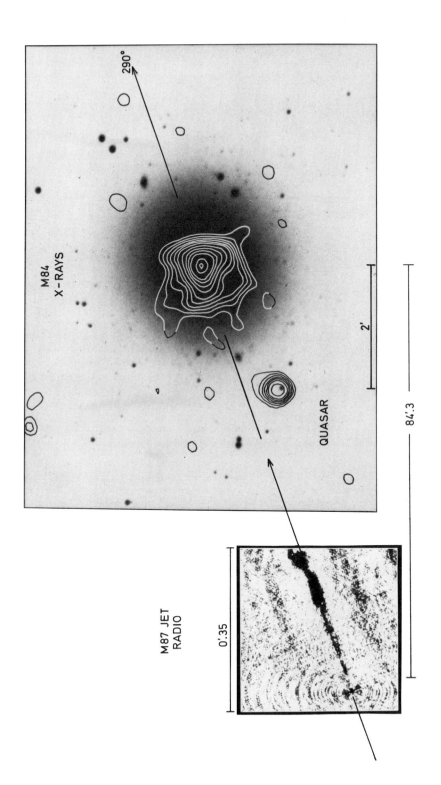

Figure 9-15(b). M84 showing compressed isophotes indicating it is traveling outward exactly along the line of the jet from M87. (Insert to lower left shows radio map, on an enlarged scale, of the jet in M87).

M84
X-RAYS

QUASAR

290°

2'

84'.3

M87 JET
RADIO

0'.35

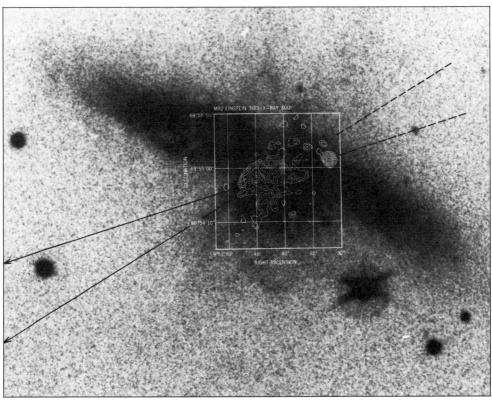

Figure 9-16. X-ray map of the interior of M82. The direction to the line of quasars discussed in Chapter 4 is shown.

moving out along this line. The knots in the jet of M87 would then represent the proto-galaxies now being ejected out along this line. I would consider that there could be no more conclusive proof of the radical hypothesis made in the 1950's that galaxies are born from matter which is ejected from other galaxies.

Another line, or perhaps cone, of ejected material coming from an exploding galaxy is seen in M82, the peculiar companion of the large, nearby spiral M81. As shown in Figure 4-12 and 4-13, four quasars emerge from the nucleus of M82 in the same direction as the inner X-ray material. Figure 9-16 shows how over a larger field, and in more detail, this X-ray material extends from the nucleus of M82 outward along the line of quasars. It is true that one filament of X-ray material extends out along the minor axis in the direction of the optical emission filaments. *But the main body of the interior X-ray emission is extended systematically at an appreciable angle to the apparent minor axis and very closely along the line to the quasars.* In hydrogen maps of M82 (not shown here) three hydrogen condensations are also seen along this line to the quasars. The alignment of these three hydrogen clouds is rotated slightly from the line of the quasars, a configuration we see is characteristic from the examples discussed in the previous chapter. It is interesting to note, in detail, that some of the small pieces of X-ray material lie directly along the line of ejection to the quasars. The extension of the ejection cone backwards, in the opposite direction, also passes closely along X-ray material in that direction and nearly includes an intense, compact source of X-ray emission which is optically unidentified. All of these recent observations furnish rather precise and detailed confirmation of a conclusion about ejection of physical material, compact objects and quasars for which the evidence has been building up for more than 20 years.

It is difficult to say at this point what the X-ray evidence means in terms of the physics of ejection. Does the X-ray emission really signify high temperatures? Could it be caused by rapid deceleration of fast-moving, low-mass particles? Or could it arise from transitions in atomic states too tightly bound to be normally observed? More X-ray spectra and more sensitive observations need to be obtained. X-ray observations should be made in a larger areas around galaxies like M82, larger than the small interior regions presently mapped. Deep radio mapping over larger areas around the galaxy and systematic, deep quasar surveys need to be made. All the key objects discussed in this book need to be observed more intensively. We need to follow through and obtain evidence which will help us understand the actual physical mechanisms responsible for the new phenomena we have seen.

In fact, in the entire subject of extragalactic astronomy what is needed are serious, systematic surveys of certain kinds of key objects like ejecting galaxies, X-ray sources, and quasar associations all over the sky. It is time astronomers stopped taking a part of one object, or a small sampling of another kind of object, and simply using these small samples to calibrate their preconceptions. It is time they stopped ignoring the simple, obvious evidence that contradicts their current assumptions and indulged in a little old-fashioned, hard observing work.

K. Comments on Future Observations

To single out one object as an example, for further research, we can comment on NGC 3842 in Figure 9-14. The most important next step to take in this critical object is to observe spectroscopically the further quasar candidates I have identified close to NGC 3842. Will the group of confirmed quasars around the galaxy grow in number? It will be of critical importance to examine with greater sensitivity and resolution whether there are any X-rays from the center of this galaxy and whether X-ray emission from the quasars is linked back to the galaxy.

It will also be important to systematically search the whole field of this cluster of active galaxies for additional quasars. The presence of a group of point X-ray sources around another bright galaxy in the cluster, NGC 3860, is shown in Figure 9-14. Point source X-ray emission is one of the clues to the presence of quasars. The existence of this group of point X-ray sources was effectively disguised in the presentation of the original X-ray data. It represents a potentially crucial object. What is this group of sources?

Further observations in this region, however, will be difficult to obtain. To illustrate this point, it should be noted that when the X-ray observations were published it was obvious the blue stellar objects lying so spectacularly close to the galaxy were quasars. But this fact was not mentioned by the X-ray astronomers who published the data, despite the fact that the most widely known issue in astronomy was the well-known prediction that quasars appear much closer to galaxies than can be accounted for by chance. While I was still a staff member, I applied for time to confirm them as quasars, but I was turned down by the Palomar time-allocation committee. I only squeezed them in incompletely on my last run and then needed the help of friends at other observatories. Publication of the simple fact that the objects are quasars was held up for about a year and a half. When they were published, one X-ray astronomer violently protested to the editor of the *Journal* my implying that the X-ray quasars were associated with the other strong X-ray sources which were associated with the NGC 3842 cluster of galaxies.

Since the people who make these kinds of observations have now been excluded from regular observations on the telescope, how does one obtain these kinds of observations? How can one confirm critical new quasars such as the candidates near NGC 3842? How can one measure the magnitudes and redshifts and obtain complete area surveys which are so useful and necessary? The known history of this situation is also a vivid warning to anyone else who is tempted to undertake these kinds of observations in the future.

It is clear there is a vested political interest in suppressing these kinds of observing projects. A freeze on these kinds of observations will continue until a courageous director or the staff of some observatory sees that there is an opportunity to make a notable advance in science and allows interested individuals to investigate these important problems. That this will be a difficult step to take, even at one or two institutions, I think may be illuminated by the following chapter which attempts to deal with the emotional and professional motivations in the field.

Appendix to Chapter 9

The first important deductions about ejection from galaxies and possible connections with galaxy origin were contributed by V. A. Ambartsumian. Later, B. E. Markarian established the statistical reality of galaxy chains. References to their works are given below in a paper in which I investigated the connection of these galaxy alignments with lines of radio ejection. This paper also presents the basic observations for the origin of galaxies in ejection lines.

1968, Arp, H., Publications of the Astronomical Society of the Pacific, 80, p. 129.

A later summary of ejection phenomena in galaxies and their possible connection with the birth of new galaxies is given in:

1978, Arp. H. "Ejection from Galaxies and Galaxy Formation." in Problems of Physics and Evolution of the Universe. published by the Armenian Academy of Sciences, Yerevan, Armenia.

This is a volume of articles published to honor the Soviet academician, V. A. Ambartsumian. Since one of his contributions to astronomy was his brilliant, early analyses of ejection phenomena in galaxies, and, since mine was an invited paper, I felt that I could speak more freely than usual and state matters in a way which would not have been allowed in technical journal publications. This article provides full references to material on this subject preceding this date.

Resolution-enhanced pictures of the jet in M87 are given in:

1976, Arp, H., and Lorre, J., Astrophysical Journal, 210, p. 58.

Evidence that the knots in the M87 jet are variable in brightness and a comparison of their properties to the quasar related, BL Lac objects is given in:

1979, Arp, H. and Sulentic, J. W., Astrophysical Journal, 233., p. 44.

The counterjet in M87 was first described in:

1967, Arp, H., Astrophysical Letters, 1, p. 1.

Additional data on gaseous emission features and theories about their "raining" down on M87 were discussed in:

1979, Butcher, H. and Ford, H., Astrophysical Journal Supplement, 41, p. 147.

The latest paper on the emission filaments in the halo of NGC 5128 is published in:

1981, Graham, J. A. and Price, M., Astrophysical Journal, 247, p. 813.

This paper includes references to the earlier, extremely beautiful photographs of NGC 5128 taken with the 4-meter Cerro Tololo reflector in Chile.

One possible mechanism for producing narrow, straight filaments such as those observed in NGC 5128 might be to have a small cloud of dust or gas drift into the edge of an outgoing beam. Large aligned filaments such as observed in the counterjet in M87, however, probably still strongly require the ejection of material aggregates of matter. Also the secondary expansion of ejected objects is probably necessary to account for the lumps of hydrogen emission along the ejection track as observed in the radio galaxy 3C 277.3 by:

1985, van Breugel, W., Butcher, H., Miley, G., Heckman, T., and Bridle. A., Astrophysical Journal, 290, p. 496.

Recognition that the observations required the ejection of compact bodies from galaxies was made by Valtonen in his discussion of slingshot mechanisms to eject black holes from active nuclei. More recently it has been argued that extended radio lobes contain secondary hot spots which are energized by the primary hot-spots. This is discussed in:

1984, Valtaoja, E., Astronomy and Astrophysics, 140, p. 148.

The observations of quasars and quasar candidates in the center of the Virgo Cluster are given by:

1984, He. X. T., Cannon, R. D., Peacock, J. A., Smith, M. G. and Oke, J. B., Monthly Notices Royal Astronomical Society, 211, p. 443.

X-ray observations of Virgo cluster galaxies are reported in:

1985, Forman, W., Jones, C., and DeFaccio, M., Conference on Virgo Cluster held at European Southern Observatory. Munich, September 1984, p. 323.

See also these conference proceedings for radio maps of the Virgo Cluster by Kotanyi which show a core of E galaxies and a hollow oval of spirals (p. 13).

A recent discovery of a quasar within 0.3 arcsec of the nucleus of a low redshift spiral galaxy is given by:

1985, Huchra J., Gorenstein, M., Kent, S., Shapiro, I., Smith, G., Horine, E., and Perley, R., Bulletin of the American Astronomical Society, 16, No. 4, p. 1005.

By far the largest and latest compilation of chains of galaxies is included in:

1987, Arp, H., and Madore, B.G., "Catalogue of Southern Peculiar Galaxies and Associations," Cambridge University Press.

Photographic examples are given in Volume II of this catalog. The most recent review of excess redshift of spiral galaxies in groups is given in:

1984, Giraud, E., "Galaxies Normales Autour du Flot de Hubble," Thesis, Academie de Montpelier, Université des Sciences et Techniques du Languedoc, France.

Early references to theories of spiral structure as caused by ejection and connected companions appear in:

1969, Arp, H., Sky and Telescope, 38, p. 385.

1969, Arp, H., Astronomy and Astrophysics, 3, p. 418.

The very important analysis of radio ejection in the spiral galaxy NGC 4258 and its possible relation to the formation of spiral arms is given in:

1972, van der Kruit, P. C., Oort, J. H., and Mathewson, D. S., Astronomy and Astrophysics, 21, p. 169.

A recent discussion of the origin of spiral arms is given in:

1986, Arp, H., "The Persistent Problem of Spiral Galaxies," IEEE Transactions on Plasma Science, Special Issue on Space and Cosmic Plasma, December 1986.

The most detailed X-ray map of M82 is published in:

1985, Kronberg, P., Biermann, P., and Schwab, F.R., Astrophysical Journal, 291, p. 693.

The situation with the X-ray observations in the galaxy cluster A1367 can be gleaned with some difficulty from:

1983, Bechtold, J., Forman, W., Giacconi, R., Jones, C., Schwarz, J., Tucker W. and van Speybroeck, L., Astrophysical Journal. 265, p. 26.

Credits for Pictures used in this Chapter

Figure 9-1. Photograph by Arp with 200-inch. Image processing for high resolution in insert by Jean Lorre.

Figure 9-2. Photograph in ultraviolet by J.-L. Nieto with the Canadian-French-Hawaiian Telescope.

Figure 9-3. Photograph by Arp with 200-inch in blue emission line (O II). Below is radio map with Very Large Array (VLA) by Owen, Hardee, and Bignell.

Figure 9-4. Photograph by J. Graham with CTIO 4-meter in red hydrogen emission line.

Figure 9-6. Radio map of CEN A by cooper, Price, and Cole, with Parkes Antenna. Deep photograph of NGC 5128 by R. D. Cannon with U. K. Schmidt telescope (courtesy of Royal Observatory, Edinburgh).

Figure 9-8. Photograph from *Catalogue of Peculiar Galaxies and Associations*, by Arp and Madore, published by Cambridge University Press.

Figure 9-12. Radio map by van der Kruit, Oort, and Mathewson with Westerbork Array.

Figure 9-13. Adapted from radio map in neutral hydrogen by S. Gottesmann with the VLA.

Figure 9-15. X-ray map by Einstein Observatory, courtesy Forman, Jones, and DeFaccio. Radio map of jet (lower left panel) by Owen, Biretta, and Hardee with VLA (National Radio Astronomy Observatory is operated by Associated Universities, Inc., under contract with the National Science Foundation.)

Figure 9-16. X-ray map from Einstein satellite observations, courtesy of P. Kronenberg and P. Biermann.

THE SOCIOLOGY 10 OF THE CONTROVERSY

We are about to come to the last chapter, where we have the pleasant prospect of considering what the evidence so far discussed might mean. Before we reach that point, however, I should try to address the question of why so much opposition to this evidence has arisen. This sociology of the redshift controversy may illuminate the effectiveness of the way scientists interact in their attempts to advance knowledge.

When I first began astronomical research in the early 1950's, there were relatively few astronomers, perhaps only numbered in the hundreds of active astronomers rather than the thousands of today. But even in those days, where there was a concentration near the large telescopes on the west coast of the U.S., there was keen competition and rivalry. Some individuals attempted to protect "territory" in certain areas of research. Individuals competed for discoveries, priorities for theories, and telescope time. Of course, comradery between researchers working on different aspects of the same problem also existed as well as a certain amount of observatory loyalty and regional loyalty. What seemed to make all this very productive was

that the researchers generally could follow up the most important astronomical questions, spent the great bulk of their time personally making observations, and could announce results or follow new lines of research without fear of endangering their positions. But it was always very competitive in the sense of professional recognition.

I personally remember the pleasure of making observations on long-term projects which were fundamental contributions to astronomical data. From time to time, an observation would confound current expectations. That was particularly exciting because it meant that something new and important might be discovered. Of course, sharp debate about the reality and significance of the new results usually followed. In general, informed debate improved understanding and spurred progress. But the right side did not always win. For example, my discovery that the Magellanic Clouds, neighboring galaxies to our own Milky Way, have chemical compositions different from our own Galaxy was attacked. Later, when it was found to be true, the result was attributed to other researchers. Such events happened occasionally in the field. In any case, by that time the apparent anomalies in redshifts of quasars and galaxies were appearing and they promised to have much more far-reaching implications. Looking back now, however, it seems to me that the seeds of disruption, particularly at my own observatory, had already been sown, at that time by excessive competitiveness.

The crucial battleground for this was the committee which was appointed each year to apportion observing time on the telescopes. The rationale of the committee was the very persuasive one that large telescopes were the unique scientific resource of the observatory and should be used on the most valuable and worthy scientific observing programs. Senior staff regularly sat on the committee and considered it their responsibility to see that, of all the programs submitted, only good programs were allowed time and that more time was given to the best programs. But somehow or other the first prize was regularly won by the committee members' own programs. My personal opinion, on the other hand, was that because we were dealing with frontier levels of research, that it would be extremely difficult, if not impossible, to select the programs that would ultimately prove the most valuable. Committee members who held certain scientific tenets would necessarily take a dim view of programs which did not subscribe to these beliefs or set out to test them. But these programs might be the most important programs of all! Since a discovery is by definition a surprise the committee was, in a way, trying to eliminate discoveries. This was even recognized after a fashion. For example. one of the largest users of telescope time was in the habit of remarking cynically, "Well, nobody actually observes what they say they are going to observe in their proposal."

During some of the times I served on the committee, I observed at first hand many of the factors overriding the objective criteria of what research programs were best. The forceful personalities of some individuals, un-spoken understandings between members, tactics by many in asking for much more time than they expected to receive—all are characteristic of such committees and heavily influence its decisions.

The major sociological dynamic I observed was that those observers awarded the most time would be perceived to be the most important and influential. This, rather than the science, often became the prime motivation for winning more and more time. To me it marked the start of the dissolution of the society of equals. The prophecy was made, the round table and Camelot crumbled, perhaps because there was no King Arthur. But given the reality of the imperfection of human institutions, the committee could still have worked relatively well if the principle of minimum observing time had been respected. To reduce the observing request of a bona fide observatory staff member below a certain level would obviously prevent him from carrying out his research function and violate the concept of scientific tenure.

I think I understand well the almost irresistible temptation to try to cut out completely someone else's incorrect research, particularly if that research attracted public attention away from one's own, more deserving research. I was proud of the fact that my colleagues resisted this temptation. I, in turn, tried to make my research as accurate as possible even with reduced telescope time, publish in the accepted journals and claim cautiously only directly provable consequences of the observations. (For example, I have never before argued directly for specific physical interpretations as I do in the final chapter of this book.) I took great joy in discovering and arguing for observational results that could force important changes. I was agonized whenever there were attempts to discredit the observations. But above all, I trusted that the process could continue so that the facts could speak for themselves and all scientists and others interested in the subject would have a chance to decide for themselves what they wished to believe about their universe. This status prevailed for about two decades when the situation suddenly fell apart with appalling suddenness.

I had tried to make a customary tennis date with an old and valued Caltech friend who had been a long-time opponent on the subject of quasars. He was embarrassed and evasive. On the following day, the six-person telescope allocation committee, of which he was a member, sent me an unsigned letter stating that my research was judged to be without value and that they intended to refuse allocation of further observing time. In all honesty I must say that in my life the sun would never shine as brightly or the morning smell as fresh after this day.

News of this denial of telescope time spread with amazing rapidity. A front-page article appeared in the *Los Angeles Times* based on the letter which had been released by the new director of my observatory upon the request of the newspaper. Soon, copies of that article and others on the same subject were hanging on bulletin boards of observatories all over the world. A number of directors of other observatories as well as other well-known astronomers communicated to the director of my observatory strongly supporting my research and opposing the action of the allocation committee. I challenged members of the committee to debate the actual scientific facts. But none of this prevented the inevitable last act. My observations on the 200-inch telescope at Palomar terminated in 1983, and at Las Campanas in 1984.

What led to this sudden change from the previous equilibrium? It seems to me there are both general causes involving developments in the field overall and specific local developments associated with the institutions I was connected with. I will comment on the local issues first and then go on to the more general issues.

Carnegie Institution of Washington was the initial builder of large telescopes in the world. The 60-inch followed by the 100-inch on Mount Wilson enabled Edwin Hubble and other Carnegie Institution staff members to produce many of the early fundamental results in extragalactic and stellar astronomy. When these same astronomers initiated plans for the 200-inch at Mount Palomar during the 1930's, the bulk of the money was available only from the Rockefeller Foundation. But rather than give the money to Carnegie Institution, that Foundation actually vested ownership of the Observatory in Caltech. Caltech had no astronomy faculty at that time, so it was the Carnegie side who actually supplied the astronomers and the observatory was operated under a joint agreement between Carnegie Institution and Caltech. Even by 1948, when the 200-inch telescope began operation, the astronomy department at Caltech was barely starting. The first Ph.D.'s from Caltech were graduated in 1953; Allan Sandage, Helmut Abt, and I were the first three to emerge from the program. Sandage became a Carnegie Institution staff member in 1953 and I joined the staff in 1957.

The Mount Wilson and Palomar Observatories, as it was called in those days, was a most prestigious and desirable place to work. It operated under a succession of three directors, Ira Bowen, Horace Babcock, and terminally, Maarten Schmidt. Starting with Bowen, who was from Caltech, it was informally expected that directors from Caltech and Carnegie would alternate. For more than thirty years it was probably the leading single observatory in producing astronomical research. Then on 1 July 1980, Caltech broke the agreement and took over sole operation of Palomar Observatory.

Carnegie staff members who had been voting faculty members at Caltech for tenures of up to 27 and 23 years had their faculty positions terminated. The two most astronomically productive staff members were associated with the Carnegie Institution of Washington. They no longer observe at Palomar. These are the facts. As in some other astronomical activities, the facts are open to a wide variety of interpretations. Perhaps the best I can do is select a few additional facts which may illuminate these specific events somewhat and then pass on to more general comments.

The committee which allocated telescope time on the telescopes at Palomar and on Mt. Wilson and in Chile (the latter two telescopes being Carnegie's) continued to be a joint committee of Caltech and Carnegie Institution of Washington, even after the breaking of the agreement of joint operation of the Observatories. From about the time of the breakup and afterward, the two most senior Carnegie astronomers did not serve on this allocation committee. This interval included the year in which the committee issued the letter condemning my research and the following year in which they denied my application for 200-inch Palomar time. Less senior members of the Carnegie staff served on the allocation committee, received telescope allocations on the 200-inch telescope, and continued informal cooperation with Caltech.

Perhaps this is the time to switch to general comments. Any discussion of something new requires dialogue between hypothesis and criticism. If animated and vigorous this is controversy. It is supposed to uncover what is wrong and illuminate what is correct, or possibly correct. The more energetically this process goes on, the more progress can be made, particularly if further testing is stimulated. Controversy can be extremely valuable. But some people on the other side of the present controversy have denied that there was a legitimate controversy. They insist that the issues were all resolved long ago, that no valid evidence of new effects exists, and that further discussion or testing is a waste of time. In that case, the preceding nine chapters of this book are totally wrong. In that case, perhaps the termination of tenure is correct. Each reader will have to judge for himself. But in my opinion, as long as even the possibility of a valid observational discrepancy exists, there is a strong imperative to allow the process of free scientific inquiry to examine it. In no case is it scientifically permissible to bar research on a single specific subject.

What are the rewards of paying attention to observational discrepancies and what are the penalties of dismissing them? Here is a piece of real history which I happen to know about because it was told to me by one of the participants. It dramatically illustrates the critical role of discordant evidence:

Picture yourself during the early 1920's inside the dome of the 60-inch telescope on Mount Wilson. One of the men who had driven the mules that carried the pieces of that same 60-inch telescope up the old Mount Wilson trail was Milton Humason. Humason stayed on at the observatory to become janitor and then night assistant on the telescope. (Eventually he became secretary of the Observatory and a delightful and famous astronomer.) Humason was by then an observing assistant, and we can picture him talking to the well-known Carnegie Institution astronomer, Harlow Shapley, in that dome. Humason is showing Shapley stars he had found in the Andromeda Nebula that appeared and disappeared on photographs of that object. The famous astronomer very patiently explains that these objects could not be stars because the Nebula was a nearby gaseous cloud within our own Milky Way system. Shapley takes his handkerchief from his pocket and wipes the identifying marks off the back of the photographic plate.

Of course, Hubble came along in 1924 and showed that it was just these Cepheid variable stars in the Andromeda Nebula which proved that it was a separate galaxy system. This discovery enabled Hubble to make the most fundamental revolution in science of our time.

This story suggests many conclusions. One is that telescopes do not make great discoveries, people make great discoveries. Moreover, people make great discoveries by noticing something that should not be there, but is, and then following it up. How would history have changed if Shapley had seriously looked at those objects he had been shown?

After he went to Harvard, Shapley researched these same Cepheid variables and thus calibrated the distance scale of Hubble's universe.

But was it the right scale? Now it was Walter Baade in the 1940's, working with the 100-inch reflector on Mount Wilson, who paid heed to the fact that the age of the universe from Hubble's expansion law was less than the age of the earth's rocks derived from geological evidence. He also noticed that the Cepheid variable stars that Shapley had observed in globular clusters were different from the Cepheids in the Andromeda Nebula. Thus, Walter Baade, by paying attention again to discrepancies, used the telescopic observations to enlarge the scale of the Universe and make another fundamental astronomical advance.

When we got the first color-magnitude diagrams of globular clusters, we found the stars did not evolve straight up the main sequence as they were supposed to. This led Allan Sandage and Martin Schwarzschild to enunciate the theory of stellar evolution which has been of such enormous importance to astronomy ever since the early 1950's.

But it is the people who make the discoveries and initiate new directions. If the people are not allowed to pursue their programs the consequences can be very destructive not only for the science but also for the institution which is trying to do science. An example of this follows from the continuation of the Shapley story.

History as the way it was saw Shapley leave Mt. Wilson to become director of Harvard College Observatory. When I graduated from Harvard in 1949, Shapley was just retiring as director. There was internal competition and Bart Bok, the astronomer who almost everyone assumed would be the new director, found himself with his observing facilities cut off. Bok then founded a new observing facility at Harvard to observe radiation from the hydrogen gas that is so prevalent in the Universe. That particular radio astronomy technique became one of the powerful new tools of astronomy. But it was impossible for Bok to stay. He left, helped to found a flourishing development of optical astronomy in Australia, and inspired many young astronomers. He then returned to the University of Arizona for similar achievements and died a few years ago, one of the most beloved of astronomers.

Meanwhile, the radio astronomy Bok had started at Harvard was shut down and Harvard astronomy went into a generation of relative eclipse from which it has only recently recovered with the advent of X-ray and satellite astronomy.

This last lesson seems to me to be that if the goals of research are subordinated to any other consideration, this can lead to the rapid decline of excellence in even the most prestigious institutions. In some respects, this might be a natural and healthy cycle, with old centers decaying after a generation or so, and subsequently new centers of innovation and excellence springing up in other parts of the world. One danger today however, is that with science tied increasingly closely to expensive equipment, which in turn is tied to prominent institutions, that science may progress much less rapidly than its potential. If any useful data leaks out of these ponderous undertakings they may be only synthesized elsewhere. In fact, it might even become so that, as in the arts, the truly most creative and important achievements in science will not take place within the universities or institutions at all.

I am moved to think of Sir Fred Hoyle. His brilliant scientific career has been involved with many controversies. At one time, he was director of the Institute of Theoretical Astronomy in Cambridge, England. But in spite of, or perhaps because of, his being one of Britain's leading scientists and intellectuals, certain academic maneuvering took place and he resigned the directorship. For a long time, in a most productive part of his career, he has produced his superb, ground-breaking science from his own house in northern England. A few years after the resignation, I was dining at high table in one of Britain's most noted Colleges. The don on my left enquired during dinner whether I knew Fred Hoyle. When I said I did and that I thought highly of him, this professor looked around furtively, lowered his voice to a whisper, and said, "He is a great scientist who was treated very badly around here." The statement did not surprise me, but I can never forget the fearful whisper in which it was spoken, as if we were in some kind of occupied country.

One colleague characterized the situation in the following way: Some scientists have a strong interest in, and talent for research. Other scientists are more oriented toward the rewards and problems of interacting with people. The latter tend toward administration and science politics. Of course, science has had some visionary leaders who were not principally researchers but who were of enormous value to the field. But it is probably true that if rivalry arises between members of these groups, the researcher has little or no short-run protection. And who is to say that those who control institutions should not hire people who think as they do? But if institutions become too large or fashionable to tolerate research outside the mainstream, then the best research may come to be done by people not trained or working at these institutions. Will this signal a change in the way fundamental science is accomplished, a direction opposite to the way modern, big science has increasingly gone?

It is not so long ago that science was not done in institutions, to put it mildly! Everyone is well aware of the "discomfort" that the 17th century church visited upon Galileo. But when the present Pope encouraged further investigation of this little unpleasantness, two interesting points turned up: One was that some lesser known academics of a different viewpoint at neighboring universities had probably encouraged the church to discipline Galileo. Secondly, no individual officer of the Vatican had ruled on what the truth was or was not.

Galileo had argued for the coexistence of two authorities—an experimental authority for science and the Bible for everything else. This amiable view made no impression on the Vatican, however, because his recantation was directed by the authority derived from the Edict of the Council of Trent. That august committee, sitting more than a century before, had decreed that in all matters in which the Bible stated the nature of physical events, that the Bible had to be accepted as *literally* true. No other interpretations were permitted.

The ruling of this committee was used as the final authority against the new Copernican science. It is interesting that it was not only science that the Council of Trent was trying to suppress. In his opera "Palestrina," Hans Pfitzner dramatized the attempt of the papacy to hold back the developing art forms of polyphonic music. He also succeeds in dramatizing the intolerance and hypocrisy beneath the holy apparel. Of course, we all think of the Galileo incident, with its overtones of the threat of torture and recantation, as having taken place in some remote, barbaric age in the far past. But that is not so; as far as his life span goes, Galileo could have been a faculty member at Harvard.

The point is that this is so short a time ago. Authority in the field of natural philosophy—that is, the nature and origin of the Universe—has since passed from the church to science. But human beings, the people who make up such institutions, have they changed that much in this relatively short span of time? How much does the social structure today promote or even protect significantly different viewpoints?

Most important are the consequences we might foresee for the far future. The rigidifying of the inquiring spirit in the research institutions of the West must have an ultimate effect on our society. After all, the most advanced nations and alliances in history were dominant no longer than 500 to 1000 years. Events may evolve more rapidly today. How would a decline occur in our present era? I think it might well have its first tangible effect in science because science is the single most important factor in the power of a society today.

If a new culture or group or even diverse individuals were to attain greater influence, it would be because of fresher, more effective science and learning. That of course could only be relative to stagnation of these values in the current centers. If an excessive competitiveness, or an excessive interest in political power or prestige, atrophies learning and science in one place, the opposite values of idealism, cooperation, and interest in the science itself will cause it to rise in other places. This seems to be for the far future, but I cannot help wondering if we are beginning to see the inexorable break-up of the current ways in order to make ready for that future.

Be that future as it may, however, we are now in a position to do the most exciting thing we could do at the present moment—look at observational evidence and see if we can form a coherent picture which is an advance over the old.

But before we go to that final discussion, I want to pay tribute to all those scientists that I have known and worked with who were sincerely dedicated to finding out what the universe was really like. They worked hard, argued passionately, and were gracious in both victory and defeat. In particular, I salute those scientists who, in spite of disagreeing strongly with another researcher's views, were nevertheless meticulously fair, helpful in advancing the research, and assisted in publication and discussion of the results. May the numbers of this group grow and prosper.

Appendix to Chapter 10

An interesting and informative discussion of the attitudes toward cosmological theories, past and present, is given in the book:

1984, Pacholczyk, A. G., The Catastrophic Universe, Pachart Publishing House, Tucson.

The book above also includes a discussion of, and references to, the recent investigations of the Galileo history, including the 1983 essay by O. Pedersen.

Some of the public discussion of the opposition to the investigations reported in the present book appear in:

1982, Los Angeles Times, February 15, p. 1.

1982, Science, 215, p. 1214.

INTERPRETATIONS 11

The observational evidence presented in the first nine chapters requires that objects and events in the universe are much different than has been commonly supposed. Exactly how the universe does work in detail, of course, cannot be specified with certainty at this moment. It is possible such a time can never come. Nevertheless, it will be fascinating to discuss some of the advances in understanding that might result from this new observational evidence.

A. The Empirical Results

We have emphasized previously that only one well-documented example of an extragalactic, nonvelocity redshift is required to overthrow the current assumption that all extragalactic redshifts are caused only by velocity of recession. Table 11-1 recapitulates a dozen independent proofs of the phenomenon of nonvelocity redshift explored in this book. The table has been arranged in its present form in order to summarize these many different cases and also in order to fore-

stall an old game with which I unfortunately have had much experience. The game goes something like the following: "In such an important matter we want to consider only the most conclusive proof which exists. Which proof is the most conclusive? Ah yes, that one is very interesting. We will adopt that one as our *experimentum crucis*. But now, of course, there is always the remote chance that it could be an accident, and we cannot overthrow an important principle on only one example." For this reason, many separate examples are discussed in this book. Each is conclusive in its own right on the main point and furnishes independent proof of the existence of nonvelocity redshift phenomena. Overarching this, however, is the question of how all these examples relate to each other. The body of the evidence would be more comprehensible and mutually supporting if its various pieces fitted together in some physically plausible fashion. We now attempt to do that, first in an empirical way. We leave the theoretical interpretation of why the relations exist for later in the chapter.

It seems appropriate that this empirical syn-

TABLE 11-1
Summary of Proofs of Nonvelocity Redshifts[1]

	Association at Different z's	Ejection from Galaxies	Evolution from High z to Low z
1. Association of 2 and 3 quasars with galaxies	***	**	*
2. Association of single quasars— statistical	***	**	*
3. Attachments of quasars by jets and filaments	***	***	*
4. Explosive galaxies with many quasars	***	***	**
5. Distribution of quasars over the sky	***	***	***
6. Periodicity of quasar redshifts in groups	***	*	**
7. Galaxies with discordant redshifts			
a) Interacting, high z companions	***	***	**
b) Small, positive Δz's of companions	***	**	**
c) Quantization of galaxy redshifts	***	**	*
d) Local Group, M31, H I clouds	***	***	**
8. Ejection of radio, X-ray, and optical objects	***	***	**
9. Chains, radio, and S galaxies in clusters	***	*	*

[1]Proofs that I consider conclusive are given three asterisks (***); those that are probable, two asterisks (**); and those that are possible, one asterisk (*).

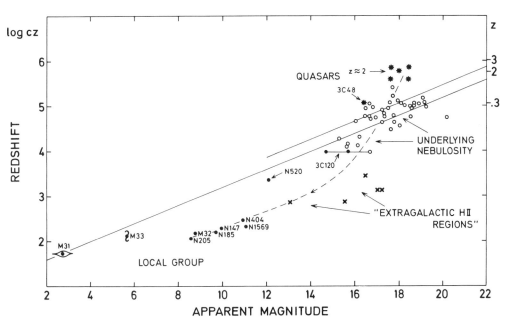

Figure 11-1. The Hubble diagram for Local Group objects as identified in the present book. Quasars are represented by asterisks. As explained in the text, the open circles represent measures of underlying nebulosity for a selection of quasar images. The radio quasar 3C 120 is variable in apparent brightness and the magnitude of its underlying disk has been estimated from Figure 8-7.

thesis turns out to be best made by using the Hubble diagram, the diagram which plots the redshift versus the apparent brightness for all the various kinds of objects we have been studying. This diagram is shown in Figure 11-1.

Starting at the lower left of the diagram we plot the closest large galaxy to us, M31. We assume the universe is expanding with a uniform expansion velocity of $H_o = 75$ km s^{-1} Mpc^{-1}. At the known distance of M31 from our point in space (692 kpc), it should have an expansion velocity of 52 km s^{-1}. We plot M31 with this velocity at its observed apparent magnitude. We do this in order to give the correct relation of M31 to more distant galaxies which have larger recessional velocities. (Small perturbations arising from a galaxy's velocity or intrinsic redshift are not an appreciable portion of the total velocity of a distant galaxy, so we ignore these effects in our M31 reference point.) Next we plot the

companion galaxies in the Local Group at their observed redshifts relative to M31. We see this occupies the lower left-hand quarter of Figure 11-1 *but in a way which clearly illustrates that redshift increases as brightness decreases for these companions.* The "Hubble line," which describes the linear relationship between a galaxy's recession velocity and its distance from us, is represented by the straight diagonal line passing through M31. The line shows how a luminous Sb spiral like M31 would appear at greater and greater distances from us. But the smaller companions to M31 obey nearly a Hubble line! If we knew nothing more about them, we would say they were less luminous than M31 and spread out at variously larger distances in space from us than is M31. But, in fact, we happen to know these companions as a group are at the same physical distance from us as M31. Therefore, their *intrinsic-redshift,* apparent-magnitude behavior only *mimics* the behavior of systems at different distances in an expanding universe.

As given in the *Revised Shapley-Ames Catalog of Bright Galaxies* by Sandage and Tammann, the relative redshifts and apparent magnitudes for the Local Group galaxies considered here have all been carefully measured and checked and there is no way of appreciably changing these values. What you see now is what you will always get in Figure 11-1, and it conclusively demonstrates an intrinsic redshift effect in a group of galaxies all at the same distance.

(One remark about much fainter, lower surface brightness systems in groups, systems that appear as if they might have been torn off the edge of a larger galaxy: Such systems can have much the same redshift as the main galaxy in a group. But the companions that are separate galaxies, formed in their own right and apparently ejected initially as compact protogalaxies or quasars, tend to have systematically higher redshifts than their main galaxy.)

We now consider the quasars which we found in earlier chapters to be physically associated with the Local Group. These quasars are represented by asterisk symbols in the upper right of Figure 11-1. They include the quasars with redshifts close to $z = 2$ and apparent magnitudes close to 18 as well as the lower-redshift quasars such as 3C 48 which were found to be characteristic of the line of quasars from the Local Group companion galaxy, M33. Lying at fainter apparent magnitudes than the quasars are small open circle symbols which represent the supposed galaxy components underlying the bright stellar nucleus of a quasar, the so-called "fuzz" around their mostly stellar-appearing images.

The actual individual measurements of components underlying quasars from the work of T. Gehren, J. Fried, P. A. Wehinger, and S. Wyckoff have been plotted in Figure 11-1 because two very important points need

to be made about them:

(1) These measures are usually claimed to be "proof" of the cosmological distance of quasars because the "underlying galaxies" obey a Hubble law relationship. This Hubble law for the brightest galaxies in large clusters of galaxies is shown as a shorter, diagonal line at somewhat brighter absolute magnitude than the lower line representing galaxies of the luminosity of M31. We see that the so-called "underlying galaxies" do not obey a Hubble line at all but instead have a much steeper slope. This has been excused as due to some of these quasars being "radio-loud" and some "radio-quiet." But in actual plotted fact the supposed underlying galaxies clearly violate a Hubble recession line.[*]

(2) The actual slope of the relation defined by the "underlying nebulosity" in the quasars is the same as the empirical relation connecting the entire magnitudes of the quasars at $z \sim 2$, $z \sim 0.3$, $z \sim 0.03$, and on down toward the smaller companions in the Local Group. The actual observations imply that there is a continuity of characteristics between all these objects. Each of these kinds of objects were previously demonstrated to be members of the Local Group of galaxies. This does not prove that there is an evolutionary connection between all these objects; nevertheless the simplest hypothesis is that the highest redshift quasars represent the youngest extragalactic material in the Local Group, and that as time goes on, their intrinsic redshift decays and their luminosity grows. It is implied that they necessarily pass through stages of lower redshift quasars like 3C 48, then on to very low redshift quasars like 3C 120.

Perhaps the larger aggregates of material such as NGC 520 eventually mature into larger companions like M33 and the smaller aggregates evolve into smaller companions

---

[*] In order to emphasize this point, we note that the entire magnitude of 3C 120, including its bright stellar nucleus, is plotted in Figure 11-1 with filled circles at different magnitudes denoting its variability. But 3C 120 is a strongly radio-emitting quasar whose "underlying galaxy" would be fainter than the plotted point (estimated by the connected open circle). This would confirm the steep slope in the open circle symbols for radio loud quasars as well as for the radio quiet quasars.

like NGC 404 through NGC 205.

The remainder of the Hubble plot in Figure 11-1 shows an apparent gap: Objects only sparsely fill in the region between the lowest redshift quasars (3C 120 at 9,900 km s^{-1}) and the highest redshift companions (such as NGC 404 at several hundred km s^{-1}). Are there astronomical objects known that fill this gap?

Yes, one group of objects has not yet been discussed in this book but represents an enigma on the conventional redshift-distance assumption. These are compact objects, sometimes almost stellar in appearance, showing gaseous emission lines with redshifts between a few hundred and a few thousand km s^{-1}. They are generally not associated on the sky with other galaxies, and are usually referred to as "isolated extragalactic H II regions." (The discovery of these objects furnishes an interesting example of how astronomical research is sometimes conducted. Fritz Zwicky called attention to compact galaxies and began to circulate lists of compact galaxies at the International Astronomical Union meetings in 1964. He published papers in the *Astrophysical Journal* on these objects in 1964. I published the first examples of these extremely compact emission line objects and discussed their relationship to other galaxies in 1965. In 1970, Wallace Sargent and Leonard Searle published observations of these kinds of objects and called them "extragalactic H II regions." The latter authors did not reference the key earlier papers, and the objects became widely known as the Sargent-Searle extragalactic H II regions).

Regardless of how they were discovered, these extragalactic H II regions represent a real embarrassment for the conventional viewpoint. In the first place, why are they not associated with other galaxies? All other kinds of galaxies are associated together in groups and clusters. The obvious answer is that they do belong to a group, our Local

Group, and the inference from their redshifts that they are more distant is incorrect. From inside our Local Group it would be natural to see them in various different directions, apparently unassociated with other large galaxies. Assuming their redshift distances, however, would place them at distances comparable to the Virgo cluster of galaxies but would position them as isolated entities throughout this volume of space, ignoring places where there were many galaxies and inhabiting regions where there were no other galaxies.

A second embarrassing property of these objects is that they seem to be very young. Even straining to create a model in which an old galaxy (albeit a highly peculiar old galaxy) just now undergoes a sudden burst of star formation does not quite work. Astronomers are gradually coming to accept them as recently formed. But the universe is not supposed to be forming young galaxies now. And even if it were to try, what material exists to form them? Where is the leftover, remnant material out of which they formed? These objects are very small, with almost all the activity concentrated in one compact, semistellar nucleus. In actual fact, they are operationally most like the compact quasars and 3C 120-like objects which we have postulated as evolving down into this region of the Hubble diagram. In Figure 11-1 a few actual representatives of this class of isolated extragalactic H II regions are plotted as crosses to show that they fit into this sparse region which we previously suggested to be the evolutionary connection between the low-redshift quasars and high-redshift companion galaxies. In this case, they would be naturally young objects.

Figure 11-1 is a picture of mostly the Local Group. The diagram presumes that the universe is expanding and that galaxies like M31 further out along the diagonal line will have similar families of evolving, higher redshift objects. Of course, their companion objects will be much fainter and generally observable only with the largest telescopes.

In summary, Figure 11-1 combines almost all the objects and phenomena we have been discussing in the whole of this book in one schematic relationship. It is ironic but appropriate that in this Hubble diagram we are able to see at the same time the refutation of the conventional viewpoint of quasars and redshifts, the reconciliation of intrinsic redshifts with expanding universe concepts, and the clear continuity of how the intrinsic redshifts evolve from high redshift quasars into low redshift companion galaxies.

It is of profound importance to recall now that for a number of classes of galaxies and extragalactic objects there was never any shred of evidence that they obeyed a Hubble relation. Sb galaxies are actually the only kind of bright galaxies to obey an accurate Hubble relation. The assumption that other kinds of objects obeyed a redshift-distance relation sprang simply from the feeling that if one kind of object did, all objects must do so. Such a generalization is an example of the oldest of logical fallacies. Nevertheless, it has become an article of faith despite the many examples of contradictory evidence we have discussed.

B. Possible Theoretical Interpretations of Intrinsic Redshifts

Before attempting to discuss theories that could explain redshifts, let me first answer in a short open letter all the people who have written me over the years communicating their favorite theories for the nature of redshifts, gravity, matter, and other fundamental properties of nature. The aspects of these letters, which I always treasured, were the writers' enthusiasm, their belief that this was an important subject, and their desire to communicate perceived insights. The backgrounds of these correspondents had a wonderful variety, from no scientific training to very sophisticated knowledge of science. But on the average, they fell far short of the professional scientists in terms of the facts they knew, their knowledge of the accepted theories, and their use of the commonly accepted language of current science. So, although I was gladdened by their interest, I was saddened by the thought that they had little chance of being right when they disagreed with established science. I was also depressed by the thought that I, by the same token, had little chance of being right when I disagreed with established science.

But then I began to realize that if some of the assumptions underlying the usually accepted theories are wrong, all of us, all brands of amateurs and professionals alike, find ourselves in the same boat, simply describing incorrect beliefs in different kinds of languages. Also I noticed that what many professionals would scathingly refer to as "crackpot theories" had something in common with their own authoritative, accepted theories. Both basically started with a theory which they felt must be true, then looked for observations that could be explained by their theory, and finally declared that their theory "explained everything." Of course, valid theories are supposed to withstand every observational test. But in practice observations which did not fit were often rejected or simply ignored.

On the other hand, there were certain kinds of scientists, amateurs and professionals alike, who reasoned instead: "Here are some observations—they seem to require a theory of a certain type to explain them—how does this theory fit with the rest of the known observations." To me, this philosophy represents the really worthwhile differentiation between people interested in science.

It is clear that I espouse here that Baconian principle of induction of general laws from a body of observed facts. It would seem obvious that if a scientist only reasons deductively from known laws then he or she can never do more than recover those laws, and will never discover anything fundamentally new.

Finally, in response to the authority problem presented by many professional scientists who have an awesome amount of scientific knowledge and competence, I can only say this: it may sometimes be that not to know one thing that is wrong could be more important than knowing a hundred things that are right.

With that preamble, let us look at what the observations are actually demanding of us. The one central, inescapable fact, the fact which represents my major disagreement with accepted theory, is that the redshifts of extragalactic objects are not totally caused by velocity. We have seen innumerable examples of this in quasars with redshifts approaching the velocity of light, of peculiar galaxies with redshifts from 1,000 to 30,000 km s^{-1} and in more normal companion galaxies in the range of a few hundred km s^{-1}. Table 11-1 summarizes this accumulation of observational proof which has been presented in the previous chapters.

Conventional theory, or recent variations of it, are not capable, in my opinion, of explaining these observations. For example, the evidence clearly indicates that quasars have been ejected from active galaxy nuclei along with radio and X-ray material. In view of the popularity that the theory of gravitational lensing is enjoying today, why not postulate instead that some gravitationally compact bodies are being ejected (your choice of their properties to account for what we observe) and that these ejected bodies are simply gravitationally amplifying objects in the far background which have a recessional velocity redshift? This seems superficially attractive, but then how do we explain galaxies with discordant redshifts? These galaxies are actually seen to be interacting with much lower redshift galaxies so they must be both together in space at the same distance from us!

What about postulating the existence of strong gravitational fields from large masses within the individual quasars and discrepant galaxies as the cause of their large redshifts? The answer is that even for prototypical quasars like 3C 48, nebulosity around the nucleus is measured at about the same redshift as the nucleus. No internal gravitational fields can be responsible for these redshifts because the gradients in these fields would give different parts of the galaxies greatly different redshifts.

Of course, there have been many variations of "tired light" theories put forward to explain cosmic redshifts. The basic idea here is very reasonable. It is simply that light from extragalactic objects travels a long way through space before reaching us. In that journey, if anything interacts with the photon or its energy decays with the passage of time, it will arrive at our telescope with a smaller energy than it started with, that is; it will be redshifted. There are many ways one could imagine this happening. One is to scatter photons off intervening material. Calculations have been made for scattering off electrons, other photons, or exotic subatomic particles both within the source or on their journey to the observer. There are many difficulties with these models but the most fundamental is this: To rob a photon of some of its energy, you must jostle or perturb it at least slightly. But that means its flight path is slightly deviated. That in turn, means the image of the object becomes slightly fuzzy. But we see no evidence for unsharpness of astronomical images. In particular, high redshift objects seem as clear and sharp as low redshift objects.

In general, no matter whether gravitational fields or collisional perturbations take energy from photons, one has to postulate a screen between us and the object which removes, in discrete amounts, the energy from all the photons coming toward us from the object. This, in turn, leads to a model of "shells" of matter around the redshifted objects. In my opinion, this is a very artificial model. Furthermore, immediately adjacent objects must have either no such shells or must have different shells; otherwise, no difference in redshifts would arise. Some theorists are continuing to work on models involving these precepts and they may well be operative in certain special situations. But in seeking the general explanation of the redshift anomalies, we have seen in the present book, I personally feel it is more fruitful to look in other directions.

It is the simplicity of the observations reported here which gives them such power. This is illustrated by the many cases in which we see a high-redshift quasar or peculiar galaxy actually physically interacting with a low-redshift galaxy. Since these two objects are at the same distance, the light travel time and travel path to us must be essentially identical for the two objects. What can cause the light from the one object to be redshifted relative to the other? We are faced with a problem where essentially all the stars, gas and dust in one object emit light which is redshifted relative to the other.

Basically this means an atom of hydrogen, for example, in the higher-redshift object, that makes a given transition from one energy state to another. must emit or absorb a photon of lesser energy than the same atom would in the lower-redshift object. What determines the transition energy between two atomic states? One factor is the relative charge between the electron and the nucleus and the other factor is the mass of the electron making the transition between the two possible orbital states. Measurements of the fine structure constant in quasar spectra rules out the possibility that the electric charges could be different. That leaves only the mass of the electron.

Could the masses of *all* the particles which go to make up the matter in the high redshift object be smaller than in the matter which makes up the low redshift object?

If this were to be so, one of the few possible differences between the two types of matter would be their times of creation. My own

very simple picture for this is that a particle acquires mass by exchanqing gravitons (technically scalar zero-mass bosons) with its surroundings. But no exchange of information can take place faster than the speed of light. So each particle, as it is born into the universe, exchanges gravitons inside a bubble whose horizon expands with the speed of light. More recently arrived matter exchanges gravitons with a smaller volume and consequently has less mass. Probably an entirely equivalent description is that on newly emergent matter, the clocks run slow. (The atoms are like small clocks with their rates governed by the mass of their electrons. Slower frequencies would immediately yield redshifted photons.) Could such a crude, qualitative scenario actually be true?

Amazingly, a rigorous, complete theory exists which permits precisely this. It is called the Hoyle-Narlikar theory of conformal gravity. It is more general than the normally used theory in that the masses of particles can depend on their positions in space and time. I made a point of asking a famous physicist some years ago whether any known observations ruled out this theory. He said, "No, but we have no need for it since our present theory explains everything." I have long felt that the observations we have learned about in this book demonstrate the need for just this more general theory.

How would it work? Assume for the moment that the two objects are close enough together so that the small difference in their spatial coordinates does not matter. The only remaining difference between them would be their relative location in time. By that I mean the high-redshift object, and all the matter in it, could have been "created" or appeared in our universe at a later time. When the material first appears, it is highly redshifted. As time goes on, it becomes more massive, larger, and its high redshift decays towards more normal values. We have here a rough description of our empirical picture of a small, high-redshift quasar evolving into a lower redshift, compact galaxy, and finally into an only slightly excess redshift, companion galaxy.

How could new matter appear in our universe? There are several ways this might come about. One possibility is that the big bang did not all detonate at one instant. That rather naive assumption of total, instantaneous creation could be replaced by a notion of retarded cores, "little bangs" presently scattered throughout space.

Matter would be emerging from the little bangs now just as it once did in the original concept of the single big bang. Actually, since we can never observe events at the initial moment of the conventional big bang, it does not qualify as a scientific theory. Separate centers of origin spaced over time, however, raise the conceivable possibility of observing events now which could test in a scientific fashion the big bang conception of the creation and initial expansion of matter in the universe.

Another way of approaching the creation of matter in recent epochs is to consider the nuclei of active galaxies. Within these nuclei, it is necessary to have a source of energy. The only current suggestion for this energy source, even though it is hotly debated, is a black hole. There are two items of interest, in the present context, about a black hole. One is that inside the intense gravitational field of a black hole, space-time is strongly curved. What this means to me is simply that our currently accepted laboratory physics cannot be extrapolated inside such an extremely singular region: We simply do not know what is going on inside a black hole. The second interesting aspect is that a "white hole" is just the time reversal of the equations which lead to a black hole. Such a time reversal does not seem to be forbidden by physics. So it seems to be possible to have the reverse of a black hole, a point in space-time characterized by the property that everything "falls out" of it. Another famous physicist once half-jokingly remarked, "In physics, if something is not specifically forbidden, it is mandatory."

The outpouring of matter from galactic nuclei is in fact what we actually observe. The commonly accepted picture of ejection of radio-emitting material is one example. A white hole, or something like it, in the active nucleus helps us to explain what we observe in several ways. First, it furnishes a natural mechanism for ejecting material out into space. There is even a mechanism, developed from theories of accretion disks around black holes, that could channel the ejected material out into two opposite directions outward along the minor axis of the disk. If particles of (initially) zero mass come out along this axis they would: (1) require little force to guide into two streams, (2) necessarily have initially the velocity of light (like photons), and (3) be likely candidates to explain the "beams of relativistic particles" which radio astronomers invoke to explain their radio jets.

But we have concluded that entire coherent assemblages of material, protoquasars and proto-high-redshift galaxies, also emerge from the nuclei of active galaxies. Could anything in the nature of a white hole also permit the emergence of "lumps" of matter? We must now be approaching questions that are so speculative that they are amusing. Nevertheless, we could make a few comments that might have some possibility of meaning. Since the interior of a white hole (or black hole) is a highly curved point in space-time, it is logical that, in the limit, it must connect to other, much different points in space time. The question is: Will matter which comes through this connection (through what John Wheeler called a "worm hole" in space) and localizes in our own universe be in the form of one particle or an aggregate of particles? For a wise man, this could be a difficult question. But consider that in a high-mass black hole, the same degree of space curvature is reached over a larger volume than in a small-mass black hole. If this were to make any difference in the matter transferred, it would logically affect the *amount* of matter thereby permitting the larger volume to transfer an aggregate of matter.

There is yet another, quite different, way of looking at the possible emergence of "new" matter into the universe. Fred Hoyle developed the concept of a "zero mass surface". If you go back in time to the creation event for our galaxy, so-called time = zero, you should encounter a surface at about 2×10^{10} light years distance where all particles have zero mass. If time existed before that epoch, then photons coming through that surface from earlier times should be scattered (thermalized) by the electrons of large cross sections at that surface and thus account for the extremely homogeneous microwave radiation background. (The so-called 3-degree black body microwave radiation discovered by Arno Penzias and Robert Wilson is supposed to be relict radiation from the big bang. As such it is the only surviving proof, of the many supposed previous proofs, of one, single big bang. But the microwave background radiation is now being observed to be so homogeneous that it seems impossible to have originated from different parts of an exploding universe that were not in physical communication at the time of their thermalization. The concept of a zero mass surface accounts nicely for that homogenous thermalization within our "subuniverse.")

But if such zero mass surfaces existed in the interiors of active galaxies, then not only photons could pass across these surfaces, but perhaps also lumps of matter. Hoyle actually discusses the passage of aggregates of stars across such a surface. They would presumably be somewhat crushed. Perhaps the wave packets which describe the particles would be almost merged. But the important thing for our consideration is that there is the possibility that aggregates of matter could come through as a collection of (initially) very low-mass matter localized in our general region of space-time.

These are just a few illustrative ways of describing how new matter might "appear" in our universe. They might be all more or less equivalent descriptions or there might be different, more rigorous descriptions forthcoming in the future. The important point in trying to interpret our new observations is that such phenomena are possible, that they are not ruled out. Then, if our observations require such mechanisms we have more confidence in following through these observations and learning more about how matter actually behaves in the universe.

Of course, these ideas—in their essence—have been glimpsed and foreshadowed by many scientists in the past. The noted physicist Paul Dirac postulated that the gravitational and atomic constants are time-dependent. This theory required intrinsic redshift in matter that changes as a function of time. Moreover, Dirac raised the possibility of two kinds of matter creation—additive creation, in which new matter appears uniformly throughout the universe, and multiplicative creation, in which new matter appears preferentially where old matter already exists. (An example would be galaxy nuclei.) The brilliant and daring steady-state theory, as enunciated by Hoyle, Bondi, and Gold in 1948, postulated the continuing creation of matter throughout an expanding universe in order to maintain a constant ("steady-state") density of matter. In fact, Hoyle's C field—C for creation—is very much like the most modern theory advanced by particle physicists for the universe—the so-called Inflationary Theory. (In this latter theory, according to my limited understanding, the universe inflates because it wants to go from one phase to another.)

But where all this discussion will probably arouse the outrage of contemporary cosmologists is not so much in the creation of matter, but in the reversal of the usually assumed scenario of galaxy formation. In the conventionally assumed picture, the big bang was followed by a hot gaseous phase of matter out of which the galaxies cooled and condensed. Even though the universe as a whole, is a white hole, everything within the galaxies has been assumed to be progressing toward black holes. It has been considered to have been going downhill all the way since star formation. But the hypothesis put forward here has small galaxies being born from large galaxies, in a cascading process that could continue eternally.

The only advantage this new hypothesis has is that it seems to be what the observations are actually telling us. From the standpoint of the conventional big-bang model of the universe, however, it does not seem like such a great modification. It seems to me that in the theory proposed here, instead of having just one point in the universe which exploded 2×10^{10} years ago, that we have many points within the fabric of space that are expanding. In this sense, the universe unfolds from within itself. I am suggesting that we have both an expanding universe and a steady-state universe, but without conventional galaxy condensation.

But what happens if a lump of newly-formed matter appears inside a galaxy? It was first assumed that it would rush outward, initially with the speed of light, and then be slowed as time went on and it gained mass. It might or might not be gravitationally captured by the parent galaxy. Detailed calculations were made for this model by Jayant Narlikar and P. K. Das. The calculations confirmed quite well the observed associations of quasars with nearby galaxies as described in Chapter 2 and elsewhere in this book. It was not true, as opponents of these observations invariably stated, that, "The observations cannot be accepted because there is no theory to explain them." Such a theory had been quite rigorously detailed and published in a major professional journal. Of course, the companion statement was always, "There is no need to modify conventional theories because there are no valid observations which contradict them." These two statements have always provided the perfect double-bind against progress in this subject.

Nevertheless there was something not quite satisfactory with the Narlikar/Das model as Narlikar and I discovered when discussing the quasars apparently ejected from NGC 1097, NGC 520, and M82 (Chapter 2) and from NGC 1073 (Chapter 9). The difficulty was that the redshift of the newly created matter stayed very high for a long portion of its lifetime. This can be seen by the fact that the volume that it is exchanging gravitons with grows much more rapidly as time goes on. Not until the material reached a few times 10^9 years of its possible 2×10^{10} years of age did its calculated redshift decrease into the redshift range of $0.2 < z < 2$ observed for quasars. But the evidence, from NGC 1097 particularly, shows that the ejection of the quasars has occurred only a few times 10^7 years ago!

This caused some rethinking and suggested the most current model which goes something like this: When a lump of matter materializes near the core of a galaxy, the dimension of its particles is large. This is so because the Hoyle/Narlikar theory requires the mass and length to vary inversely—when the mass of a particle is very small its scale is very large. The interaction cross section of this new lump is therefore initially large and it usually cannot traverse the inner medium within the host galaxy. It therefore remains trapped in orbit near the nucleus of the host galaxy. As time goes on the masses of its particles increase, becoming more like normal material and then, when it has acquired redshifts and dimensions like those of the quasars we observe, it is blown out in an ejection like those we observe in galaxies from time to time. Alternatively, the object may wander into the beam of a more continuously ejecting galaxy. The advantages of this scenario are: First, the explosive energy can come from current, white-hole-like creation of new material in the nuclei of active galaxies. Second, quasars created over a span of time in the past can have a variety of redshifts but can all be ejected at one time. Third, the quasars we see can have been ejected recently, yet can have fairly large ages which will bring them into the observed redshift ranges as calculated from the theory. This age also brings them into the range estimated for transition to more normal, compact, and peculiar excess redshift companion galaxies. One cannot help noticing that in this model an active galactic nucleus is like a plant maturing seeds in a pod and then scattering them to its surroundings. But there is a brand new and astonishing aspect to the astronomical observations as we have discussed them in this book.

C. Quantization

Both quasar and galaxy redshifts appear to be quantized. How can this be explained by the theories of matter creation that we have been discussing? Simply and naturally! Well, at least, it is possible—as opposed to the conventional theory where it is flat out impossible. The point is that quantization as a physical phenomenon is a property only of matter with at least one very small dimension. Matter on a large scale does not show quantization effects. This is why conventional theories cannot construct a mechanism for quantization of redshifts of astronomical objects.

If, however, a coherent lump of matter emerges from a region of high space-time curvature, it will necessarily be subjected to quantum conditions because its mass is close to zero. Perhaps the matter comes into existence at the lowest energy state for creation, one that is separated by a discrete interval from the next lowest permitted energy level. Or, perhaps equivalently, a small discrete interval of time, Δt, may be required before the next lump of matter can come into existence. In either case, the next lump of matter created will have a higher redshift by a certain discrete amount, Δz. As time goes on and the

redshift, z, decays, the mass difference between particles in the two lumps becomes a smaller and smaller percentage of the total mass. Therefore, the quantized difference between their redshifts becomes smaller. It is observed, as we have seen, that the redshift periodicity becomes smaller as we go to objects of smaller intrinsic redshift. It will be a fascinating challenge to try to make a quantitative theory along these lines which matches the observations. Perhaps one hint of what this theory may involve is that a hydrogen-atom-like quantization represents quite well the observed quasar redshift periodicities for quantum orbits n = 13 through n = 19.

What I have done here is to form a qualitative working hypothesis. I am pleased that the same hypothesis required to explain intrinsic redhshifts also offers the possibility of explaining the quantization of the redshifts. I am pleased when it seems to explain how the quasars arrive in the observed way outside the galaxies. It is also impressive when when the mechanism furnishes a possible cause for the mysterious ejection activity which is so commonly observed within the nuclei of active galaxies. But is is still just a working hypothesis, to be discarded or modified as further observations are made to test it. In fact, its major usefulness is probably only to promote further observations.

Yet, always the hope is that we have achieved some fuller, deeper understanding of the universe we live in. Several generations ago, when the form of spiral galaxies was just beginning to be perceived, astronomer Sir James Jeans remarked, "Perhaps the spiral nebulae represent matter poured into our universe from another universe." I think we should not be deceived by the simplicity of that statement. The human mind has the awesome ability to condense enormous amounts of observation, of experience, and of reasoning into a few economical, meaningful words. In these same words, the human imagination can also sometimes communicate a whole universe of beauty and emotion.

Appendix to Chapter 11

The most authoritative source of redshifts, corrected magnitudes, and descriptions for bright galaxies, and therefore for most galaxies in the Local Group is:

1981, "A Revised Shapley-Ames Catalog of Bright Galaxies," by Allan Sandage and G.A. Tammann, Carnegie Institution of Washington Publication No. 635, Washington, DC.

A recent paper giving the measurements of nebulosity underlying quasar images and their canonical, cosmological interpretation is:

1984, Gehrin, T., Fried, J., Wehinger, P.A., and Wyckoff, S., Astrophys. Journal, 278, p11.

An early discussion of 3C 120 and its transitional relationship between quasars and normal galaxies is:

1978, Arp, H., Astrophys. Journal, 152, p. 101.

The earliest references to compact galaxies and emission objects, later called "extragalactic H II regions," can be found in:

1964, Zwicky, F., Astrophys. Journal, 140, p. 1467.

1965, Arp, H., Astrophys. Journal, 142, p. 402.

1970, Sargent, W.L.W., and Searle, L., Astrophys. J. (Letters), 162, p. L155.

1975, Arp, H., and O'Connell, R.W., Astrophys. Journal, 197, p. 291.

Theory

The fundamental exposition of the general theory of conformal gravity which permits the mass of a particle to be a function of position and time appears in the complete and rigorous book:

1974, Action at a Distance in Physics and Cosmology, by Hoyle, F. and Narlikar, J.V.(San Francisco: W.H. Freeman).

This theory applied to a specific model, explains the observed association of quasars with galaxies in:

1980, Narlikar, J.V. and Das, P.K., Astrophys. Journal, 240, p. 401.

The development of the concept of zero mass surfaces in the universe and possible passage of stellar aggregates through them is given in:

1975, Hoyle, F., Astrophys. Journal, 196, p.661.

GLOSSARY

Absolute magnitude
The brightness that an object would have if observed from a distance of 10 parsecs.

Absorption line
Energy missing from the spectrum of an object in a narrow range of wavelengths, owing to absorption by the atoms of a particular element.

***A posteriori* probability**
The probability, after an event has occurred, that it would occur.

Apparent magnitude
The brightness that an object appears to have at its actual distance, measured in magnitudes. (The faintest stars visible to the unaided eye are about 6th magnitude, and the faintest stars and galaxies photographed in large telescopes are about 23rd magnitude).

***A priori* probability**
The probability, before an event has occurred, that it will occur.

Barred spiral
A spiral galaxy in which the spiral arms unwind from a spindle-shaped "bar" of stars that forms the galaxy's central region.

Big bang theory
The theory that the universe began its expansion at a particular point in time.

Black hole
A region within which gravatational force is so intense that no photons can escape.

Blueshift
The fractional amount by which the features in the spectrum of an astronomical object are shifted to shorter (bluer) wavelengths.

CCD
"Charge coupled device": Light-sensitive electronic chips used in modern astronomy to record and to measure the light received.

Celestial poles
The points on the sky directly above the Earth's north and south poles.

Chain of galaxies	A group of four or more galaxies that roughly form a line on the sky.
Compact source	A region emitting large amounts of visible, radio or X-ray energy from a small apparent area on the sky.
Companion galaxies	Smaller galaxies accompanying a large, dominant galaxy in a galaxy pair or group.
cz	Redshift expressed as a fraction of speed of light (c = 300,000 km sec^{-1}
Declination	An angular positional coordinate of astronomical objects, varying from 0 degrees at the celestial equator to 90 degrees at the celestial poles.
$\triangle z$	The difference between two redshifts: $z_1 - z_2 = \triangle z$
E galaxy	A galaxy with smooth, ellipsoidal spatial distribution of predominantly older stars.
Electromagnetic radiation	Streams of photons that carry energy from a source of radiation.
Electron	An elementary charged particle, a constituent of all atoms, with one unit of negative electric charge.
Emission line	A "spike" of excess energy within a narrow wavelength range, typically the result of emission of photons from a particular type of atom in an excited state.
Excited state	An orbital state of an atom in which at least one electron occupies an orbit larger than the smallest allowed orbits.
Experimentum crucis	A decisive experiment that will prove or disprove a theory.
Frequency of radiation	The number of times per second that the photons in a stream of photons oscillate, measured in units of hertz or cycles per second.
Galactic equator	The plane of our Milky Way galaxy projected on the sky.
Galactic rotation	The collective orbital motion of material in the plane of a spiral galaxy around the galactic center.
Galaxy	An aggregate of stars and other material which forms an apprently isolated unit in space, much larger than star clusters (which are normal constituents of galaxies).
Gravitational lens	An object with a large mass that bends the paths of photons passing close to it.
H I	Neutral (non-ionized) hydrogen, usually observed by radio telescopes, which detect the radio emission arising from the transition between different states of spin alignment of the atom's electron and the proton in its nucleus.
H II region	A gaseous clump of predominantly ionized hydrogen, excited by young, hot stars within it, and which therefore shows conspicuous emission lines.

Hubble's Law	The proportionality betweeen a galaxy's redshift and its apparent magnitude.
H_0	The Hubble constant that the ratio of a galaxy's redshift to its distance, often estimated from its apparent magnitude; itss value is generally taken as $H_0 = 50$ to 100 km s^{-1} Mpc^{-1}.
Hydrogen alpha line	An important spectral line originating in the hydrogen atom, often seen as hydrogen alpha line emission in H II regions.
Image processing	An analysis of images which renders contrast differences, gradient changes, discontinuites, and other systematic characteristics visible; nowadays best performed by computer algorithms applied to digitized data.
Intrinsic redshift	A redshift intrinsic to an object, not caused by the object's recession from the observer.
Jet	A linear feature, much longer than it is wide, usually straight, and inferred to arise from collimated ejection of material.
Light year	The distance light travels in one year, approximately 6 trillion miles or 10 trillion kilometers.
Local Group	The small cluster of about 20 galaxxies that includes our Milky Way and another giant spiral Sb galaxy, the Andromeda Nebula.
Local Supercluster	The largest nearby aggregation of groups and smaller clusters of galaxies, with the rich Virgo Cluster of galaxies near its center.
Magnitude	A measure of objects' brightness in which an increase by one magnitude indicates a *decrease* in brightness by a factor of 2.512.
Milky Way	Our own galaxy, a spiral galaxy in the Local Group of galaxies.
Mpc (megaparsec)	One million parsecs.
Noncosmological redshift	A redshift not caused by a velocity of recession of the source of emission.
Nonvelocity redshift	A redshift not caused by a velocity of recession o the source of emission.
North Galactic Hemisphere	The half of the sky, divided by the galactic equator, that includess the north celestial pole.
Objective prism	A wedge-shaped glass that provides small spectra fo an entire field of light sources.
Parsec	A unit of distance, equal to 3.26 light years.
Peculiar galaxy	A galaxy which does not have the standard, symmetrical form of most galaxies.
Photon	The elementary particle that forms light waves and all other types of electromagnetic radiation.
Probability of association	If no physical association exists between objects, the probability that an observed configuration is a chance occurrence.

Quantization	The property of existing only at certain, discrete values.
Quasar	A pointlike source of light with a large redshift, often a source of radio and X-ray emission as well.
Radio lobe	Radio emission from appreciable extended areas on either side of a galaxy, usually connnected to the galactic nucleus by a radio-emitting jet.
Radio source	An astronomical object that emits significant amounts of radio waves.
Redshift	The fractional amount by which features in the spectra of astronomical objects are shifted to longer (redder) wavelengths.
Redshift-distance law	The hypothesis that an object's distance from us is proportional to its redshift (the usual interpretation of Hubble's Law).
Redshift periodicity	The tendency of observed redshifts to occur with certain values at certain well-defined intervals from one another
Right ascension	An angular coordinate of an astronomical object, measured eastward around the celestial equator (0 to 24 hours) from the vernal equinox
Schmidt telescope	A telescope with both a reflecting mirror and a correcting plate which can photograph a relatively large portion on the sky without distortion.
Solar motion	The motion of the sun with respect to nearby galaxies, which includes the sun's motion around the center of the Milky Way as well as its peculiar motion within our own galaxy.
South Galactic Hemisphere	The half of the sky, divided in two by the galactic equator, that includes the south celestial pole.
Spectrum	The intensity of light from an object at each wavelength observed.
Spiral galaxy	A galaxy in which the bright stars and interstellar gas and dust are arranged in a rotating, flattened disc of matter, within which prominent spiral arms of young stars and H II regions are visible.
Steady-state theory	The theory that the universe, on large distance scales, remains forever the same.
Supernova	An exploding star, which becomes (temporarily) thousands of times more luminous than the brightest normal star in a galaxy.
Synchroton radiation	Radiation emitted by charged particles moving at nearly the speed of light whose trajectories are bent in a magnetic field.
Universe	All observable or potentially observable matter that exists.
Virgo Cluster	The nearest rich cluster of galaxies, centered in the constellation Virgo.

Wavelength	The distance between two successive wave crests in a series of sinusoidal oscillations.
White Hole	A singular region in space-time, the time-reversed analog of a black hole, from which matter "falls out".
X-rays	A particular type of electromagnetic radiation, of high frequency and short wavelength.
X-ray source	An astronomical object that emits significant amounts of x-rays.
z	The symbol for redshift, defined as the displacement of spectral features in wavelength, expressed as a fraction of the original wavelength: $z = \triangle \lambda / \lambda$
z_0	Redshift corrected for the solar motion.

INDEX